HEATHLAND RESTORATION : A HANDBOOK OF TECHNIQUES

environmental advisory unit
UNIVERSITY OF LIVERPOOL

© 1988 British Gas plc

All rights reserved. No reproduction, copy or transmission of this publication may be made without written permission.

First published 1988.

Published in England by British Gas plc (Southern), 80 St. Mary's Road, Southampton, Hampshire SO9 7GL.
Printed and bound by The Camelot Press plc, Southampton.

ISBN 0-903545-39-X.

FOREWORD

Two of the outstanding features of the U.K. landscape are its diversity and the wide variety of habitats it supports. At a time when our environment is under ever increasing pressure, it is pleasing to be able to record that methods of protecting the environment whilst still allowing development to occur are at long last beginning to receive the attention they deserve.

Heathland is especially vulnerable. By bringing together in one volume as much as possible of what has been achieved by the diverse bodies involved in heathland research and restoration, British Gas hopes to assist in its preservation for future generations – a worthwhile objective in this, the European Year of the Environment.

Chapters one and two deal with the theory behind the restoration techniques that can be used, whereas chapters three and four deal with the techniques themselves. The aim throughout has been to provide fully referenced information that will be of practical value to all those who are or will be engaged in heathland work, and to present it in such a way that the reader can readily "dip" into the parts directly relevant to his or her specific interests.

1988

HEATHLAND RESTORATION : A HANDBOOK OF TECHNIQUES

CONTENTS

1.0 INTRODUCTION

1.1   Scope of the review

The objective of this review is to provide a wide ranging appraisal of techniques available for the restoration and recreation of heathland communities. The techniques discussed are relevant to:

(a)   restoration of damaged and severely disturbed existing heathlands,

(b)   creation of heathland on bare subsoil and coarse mineral substrates,

(c)   modification of grass-dominated areas to increase heather dominance.

Where possible, the review distinguishes between techniques that are suitable for upland heaths and those that are suitable for lowland heaths.

An understanding of heathland ecology is essential to the development of successful reinstatement methods. This review is therefore intended primarily for use by those with some ecological knowledge, while at the same time providing the interested reader with background information on aspects of heathland ecology. For example, topics discussed are heathland soil profiles, and the chemical, physical and biological properties of heathland soils. Also considered are the location and species composition of buried viable seed banks, and the characteristics of seed germination and seedling establishment.

1.2   Definition and origin of heathland

The word "heath" was first applied to open, relatively treeless land-scapes often dominated by the dwarf shrub heather *Calluna vulgaris* which occurred on acid soils of low fertility. In this review, the

term 'heathland' is used in the same sense as in Ratcliffe (1977), i.e.
heathland can be broadly divided into upland and lowland types. The
altitudinal boundary between them is considered to be 250m (820 ft)
(Webb, 1986) or approximately 305m (1000 ft) (Farrell, 1983). There are
further distinctions drawn between dry and wet heaths according to soil
wetness. Wet heaths are closely related to and grade into, acid mires
and blanket peats, whereas dry heaths grade into acid grassland.

In north west Europe, heathland flourishes where there is an oceanic
type of climate, lacking temperature extremes, but with abundant and
well-distributed rainfall and generally a high humidity (Gimingham,
1972). Upland heath communities occur at various altitudes in the
mountains of southern and central Europe, Britain and Scandinavia.
Lowland heaths occur most notably in those European countries which
border the North Sea and the English Channel.

In the past, most of Europe was covered by woodland, and heathland
occurred naturally only in a few coastal and upland locations
where the combination of poor soils, humid climate and wind exposure was
unsuitable for tree growth. Everywhere else the presence of heathland
is a direct product of human activities. The expansion of heathland
started in Neolithic times when the forests were gradually cleared to
provide grazing for stock. Since then, heaths have been irregularly
burnt to prevent trees re-establishing, and to stimulate new vigorous
growth of heather for grazing.

1.3   The value of heathlands, and their gradual loss

Today, heathland vegetation is often an important element in the
landscape, both in lowland areas and in the uplands, where it is
popularly described as "heather moorland". Heathlands may not only be
visually attractive but are also of considerable value as wildlife
habitats - the plants, animals and soils having developed together over
a period of about 6000 years.

In some upland districts of England and Wales, and especially Scotland,
heathlands are still actively maintained because they are regarded as
part of an overall pattern of land-use with respect to sheep farming and
grouse-shooting.

During the last few decades, there has been a relatively widespread and
rapid decline in heathlands in Britain as their use for grazing lands
was abandoned (Figure 1.1). Much traditional use of heathland has been
replaced by forestry and reclamation for agriculture involving not only
a reduction in the total area of heathland but also considerable
fragmentation of existing heathlands. Furthermore, the remaining areas
of heathland have often been disturbed by industrial construction
developments, the extractive industries, uncontrolled fires, and erosion
by vehicles, humans and animals.

Where heathland is traditionally maintained as rough grazing or grouse
moor this is done by rotational burning and low intensity grazing. If
this traditional careful management is abandoned, natural ecological
succession, particularly in lowland heathland, will lead to colonisation
by bracken (*Pteridium aquilinum*) or by trees and shrubs such as
birch (*Betula pendula* and *Betula pubescens*), Scots pine (*Pinus
sylvestris*) and gorse (*Ulex europaeus*, *U.gallii* or *U.minor*),
and woodland may eventually develop. Often severe fire is the catalyst
starting the change to woodland. Invasion by birch and gorse after fire
may be so widespread and dense that heather does not regenerate, but
woodland develops progressively and quite rapidly (Rose, 1974).
Increase in grazing pressure may cause heather moorland to progressively
change to grassland. Table 1.1 summarises the main reasons for
degradation and loss of heathlands.

1.4   Types of heathland in the United Kingdom

On the European scale, *Calluna* heathland is an oceanic type of
vegetation, but within that, heathland in the UK varies according to
climate and gradients in local conditions.

A common gradient is increasing soil wetness, with recognisable dry,
damp and wet types of heathland. Wet heathlands intergrade with the
vegetation of acidic mires and blanket peats, whilst dry heathlands
often intergrade with acidic grassland and sometimes with basic
grassland on substrata derived from parent materials with a higher base
status (e.g. chalk, limestone, calcareous clays, sandstones etc.).

Fig. 1.1. Decline of heathland in lowland Britain (Nature Conservancy Council, 1984.)

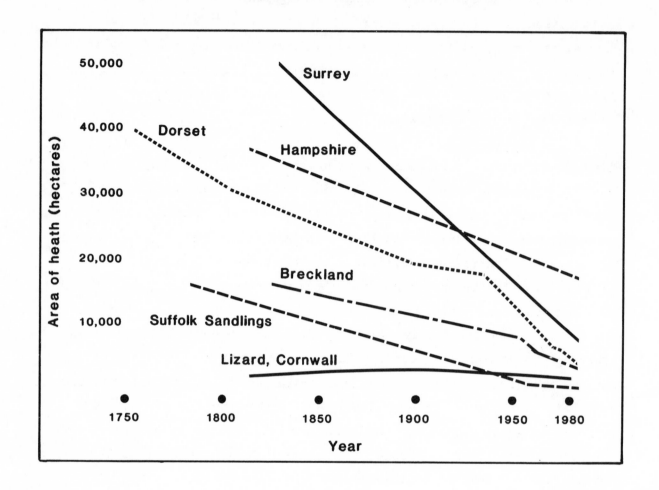

In any particular locality, there is often a continuum of types from dry heath to wet heath, bog and carr (tree dominated wetland). Particularly in the south, this may be coupled with a gradient from a nutrient-poor soil to increasing nutrient supply with increasing flushing by moving water. Thus a particular heathland locality may include a complex of wet and dry heath types, controlled by the water table. This may cause difficulties when restoration is required after a major disturbance.

There are also altitudinal heathland gradients in the British Isles with at one extreme, distinct montane and alpine heath types. These develop in the more extreme climatic conditions beyond the normal limits of forest. Many of these heathlands are fairly extensive in the Highlands of Scotland but are only fragmentary further south in the southern uplands of Scotland, northern England and north Wales.

The main heath types and their characteristic species are described below. For a fuller botanical account, the reader is referred to Tansley (1939), Gimingham (1972) and Ratcliffe (1979), and for lowland heath, to Webb (1986). A more recent account is given in the Heathlands section of the National Vegetation Classification scheme which was commissioned by the Nature Conservancy Council (NCC), and can be consulted at regional NCC offices. Throughout this review, unless otherwise stated, plant nomenclature follows that of Clapham, Tutin & Moore (1987).

1.4.1 Dry heathlands

Throughout the dry heathlands of low altitudes and upland areas (but not very high altitudes), *Calluna vulgaris* is a very frequent, almost universal, component and is often dominant.

There are relatively distinct differences between northern and southern heathlands. Upland (sub-montane) and northern communities are often characterised by an increasing proportion of grasses, which may reflect the combined effects of sheep grazing and moor-burning. A more important indicator is the increased constancy and abundance of bilberry (*Vaccinium myrtillus*), cowberry (*V. vitis-idaea*) and crowberry (*Empetrum nigrum*).

Table 1.1   Summary of kinds of degradation and losses of heathland in Britain

Reason for degradation or loss	Main locations	Major effects	Main References
Agricultural improvement	All major upland areas, e.g. Exmoor, Clwydian Hills, North Pennines, Mid Wales. Lowlands, e.g. Dorset heaths Lizard heaths.	Permanent habitat loss	Nature Conservancy Council (1977) Porchester (1977) Countryside Commission (1978)
Commercial softwood production	Heaths of S. England and uplands of Wales and Northern Britain	Fractionation and permanent habitat loss. Less planting in recent years.	Zehetmayr (1960) Countryside Commission (1978) Nature Conservancy Council (1977)
Urban development	Lowland heaths, S. England	Fractionation and permanent habitat loss	Moore (1962) Webb & Haskins (1980) Davis (1976)
Ministry of Defence use	Especially S. England, Dorset and Devon.	Disturbance and temporary (?) damage to habitat.	Green (1974)
Recreational and amenity use	Especially S. England Midlands, Yorkshire, N. Wales.	Slight to severe localised damage.	Wagg (1974), Streeter (1975), Bayfield and Brookes (1979).
Severe fire	Very widespread, e.g. S. England, Staffordshire N.York Moors, Derbyshire, Brecon Beacons.	Fractionation, disturbance and permanent (?) habitat loss	Anon. (1977)

cont'd

Table 1.1. contd.

Reason for degradation or loss	Main locations	Major effects	Main References
Pipeline installation	Especially N. Britain, Cumbria, Northumberland, Yorkshire and Dorset	Temporary or permanent damage to habitat and landscape	Moffat (1973, 1975a, 1975b) Gillham & Putwain (1977) Holliday et al (1979)
Highway construction	Scattered locations throughout Britain	Habitat damage and loss.	Putwain et al (1982)
Power industry, e.g. oil, electricity generation.	N.E.Scotland, Dorset uplands, N. Wales	Varying degrees of damage and habitat loss	Singleton (1975) SVEAG (1976)
Water industry Reservoirs	Various locations.	Permanent habitat loss	
Mineral extraction	Throughout Britain e.g. S.W.England (clays), S.England (alluvial deposits), N. Yorks (potash), Durham (fluorspar).	Extensive areas of habitat loss with associated areas of damage.	Anon. (1973) Gillham (1980) Ratcliffe (1974) Davis (1976) HMSO (1976)
Management changes	Widespread in marginal and common land e.g. N.York Moors, Cannock Chase, N. Wales, S. England.	Succession changes, invasion by bracken, trees and shrubs; loss of habitat	Rawes & Williams (1973) Rose (1974), Yates (1974), Countryside Commission (1978)

This type of community, described by Birse (1968) as 'boreal heather moor' is widespread in northern England (the Pennines, Cumbria, Northumberland, North Yorkshire etc.), North Wales and Scotland.

Lowland dry heath in southern Britain occurs on a wide variety of substrates derived from parent materials such as sands (Tertiary, glacial and wind blown), gravels, shales, sandstones, igneous and metamorphic rocks.

In sub-oceanic dry heath in southern and midland countries and East Anglia, the abundant heathers are *Calluna* and *Erica cinerea*. Gorse (*Ulex europaeus*) is widespread, and another characteristic species in eastern localities is petty whin (*Genista anglica*).   In the south and east, dwarf gorse (*U.minor*) is more common, whilst western gorse (*U.gallii*) occurs mainly in the south west of England and Wales.

Other species with restricted distributions, but which are nevertheless locally abundant, give distinct geographical character to heathlands in southern England. Significant species in this category include:

1)   Bristle bent (*Agrostis curtisii*), which occurs abundantly throughout heathlands in the south west and in some southern counties.   In these areas, *A. curtisii* replaces wavy hair-grass (*Deschampsia flexuosa*) which tends to occur in dry heathland in the Midlands and northern areas,

2)   Dorset heath (*Erica ciliaris*), which occurs mainly in Dorset heathlands,

3)   Cornish heath (*E. vagans*), which occurs on a variety of soils including serpentine soils which are rich in magnesium on the Lizard peninsula in Cornwall.

1.4.2 Humid and wet heathlands

Almost everywhere that heathland occurs there are gradients of soil wetness, varying from heath on dry freely-drained soils, through humid heath on moist soils with impeded drainage, to wet heath on soils which are waterlogged for varying periods of the year.   Where the water table is permanently at the surface and there is peat formation, the vegetation tends to be classified as valley mire.

Humid heath is generally widespread, particularly in western areas. *Calluna* tends to remain dominant but cross-leaved heath (*Erica tetralix*) is also abundant. In western southern England, Dorset heath (*Erica ciliaris*) is also associated with humid heathland. Common grass species associated with humid heath are purple moor grass (*Molinia caerulea*) and mat-grass (*Nardus stricta*).

Wet heathlands are widely distributed on peat and gley (waterlogged) soils throughout Britain (section 1.6), in both lowland and upland areas. Frequently associated with *Calluna* and cross-leaved heath (*Erica tetralix*) are various *Sphagnum* moss species – other typical species are heath rush (*Juncus squarrosus*), deer-grass (*Trichophorum cespitosum*), cotton-grass (*Eriophorum angustifolium*) and bog asphodel (*Narthecium ossifragum*). In northern moorland localities (e.g. the Pennines, North Wales, Cumbria and Northumberland) on peat, *Calluna* is commonly associated with hare's-tail (*Eriophorum vaginatum*). Other characteristic species of this heathland type are deer-grass (*T. cespitosum*), crowberry (*Empetrum nigrum*) and cloudberry (*Rubus chamaemorus*).

1.4.3 Mountain heathlands

Heathlands at the higher altitudes are fairly distinctive in species structure. In exposed habitats and on acidic soils, *Calluna* is often associated with cloudberry (*Rubus chamaemorus*), hermaphrodite crowberry (*Empetrum hermaphroditum*), bog whortleberry (*Vaccinium uliginosum*) and bearberry (*Arctostaphylos uva-ursi*). On particularly high and exposed sites, prostrate ecotypes of *Calluna* occur. These montane *Calluna* heathlands are widespread in the Highlands of Scotland and only of fragmentary occurrence elsewhere.

1.4.4 Calcareous and dune heathlands

Calcareous and dune heath are two other recognisable types of heathland (e.g. Tansley, 1939; Ratcliffe, 1977; Etherington, 1981), although they are not recognised as distinct communities in the National Vegetation Classification Scheme. If disturbance occurs, reinstatement would be

necessary to help preserve their particular biological characteristics
and their landscape value.

The calcareous heath community (see Grubb *et al.*, 1969; Thomas,
1957) consists of a mosaic of acid heath species and calcareous
grassland species, in intimate mixture.   Calcareous heath occurs on
chalk and on Devonian, Jurassic and Carboniferous limestones in England
and Wales and on various calcareous substrata in Scotland. This type of
heathland is usually small in extent since its occurrence normally
depends on the progressive development of acid surface soil horizons
which grade into base-rich lower horizons.

Chalk heath in southern England normally consists of *Calluna* or
bell-heather (*Erica cinerea*) with gorse (*Ulex europaeus*) or
dwarf gorse (*U. minor*) and other typical calcifuge species such as
tormentil (*Potentilla erecta*), mixed with calcicole species such as
salad burnet (*Sanguisorba minor*), dropwort (*Filipendula
vulgaris*) and stemless thistle (*Cirsium acaule*).   Chalk heath
occurs where shallow clay-with-flints, sands etc. overlie the chalk.

Dune heath occurs in many parts of Britain where stabilised dune systems
occur on non-calareous sands. These stable dune areas ultimately become
invaded by *Calluna* and bell-heather (*Erica cinerea*).   The sandy
soil frequently becomes podzolized (section 1.6).   The resulting
heathland has a great deal in common with inland lowland heaths on sandy
soils.

1.5   Potential for change in the species composition of heathland
       vegetation

The majority of heathlands exist as a result of the complex interactions
between the vegetation and the effects of fire and herbivores (Hobbs &
Gimingham, 1987), and their continuance depends very largely on the
management practices of burning and grazing. The species composition of
heathlands is therefore inherently unstable, and successional change
will normally follow the cessation of management. Typically, this
change is in the direction of colonisation by trees and non-ericoid
shrubs.

The rate of change depends on the availability of adjacent seed sources, the nature of the soil and the existing structure of the heath community. Where there are gaps present in an uneven-aged stand or where severe fire has occurred, invasion by birch (*Betula* spp) and gorse (*Ulex* spp) is common. Rapid colonisation by bracken (*Pteridium aquilinum*) also occurs, often advancing in from the margins of heathland. In the south, where heathland management has been discontinued, there is invasion by Scots pine (*Pinus sylvestris*) and locally by sessile oak (*Quercus petraea*). Some of the southern heathlands show all stages to the formation of closed woodland (Ratcliffe, 1977).

1.6 The soil system

1.6.1 Formation of heathland soils

Calluna heathlands are generally indicative of an acid, nutrient poor (oligotrophic) soil, in which podsolization is developed to some degree (Gimingham, 1972). Characteristically, the soil profile of a heathland podsol is very stratified and shows several distinct "horizons" (section 1.6.2).

Not only is the parent material acidic, but so is the litter deposited by the heath plants and the raw mor humus (peat) formed from it. Under the relatively cool and wet conditions of the oceanic climate, decomposition is rather slow and incomplete. Also, deep-burrowing earthworms avoid acid habitats (Dimbleby, 1962; Gimingham, 1972). For this and other reasons, the humus, instead of being mixed in well down the profile, accumulates on the surface, where humic acids are produced. These acids dissolve in rainwater as it drains downwards, and on contact with the mineral particles they mobilize iron and aluminium oxides and also other elements which are plant nutrients (potassium, calcium, phosphorus. etc.). These are washed out ('leached') from the upper layer of the mineral material. This horizon often stands out in the profile as a whitish or ash-coloured band because of the removal of iron which normally gives the mineral particles an orange-brown colour. Below it the substances (humus, iron, etc.) carried by the water draining through the profile are deposited, producing bands of dark-coloured humus and orange-brown iron. Sometimes the iron deposition is so intense as to produce a thin but hard 'iron pan'.

Heathland occurs on a wide variety of parent materials including fluvio-glacial sands and gravels, glacial tills, weathered rock debris, oligotrophic brown earth soil and peat. The substrata of lowland heaths are mainly of coarse sand. Those of the upland heaths are often of mixed stones, sand and clay and are highly compacted (Zehetmayr, 1960). In these compact soils, percolation is slower and the depth of the profile may be much less than in lowland heath soils, but a thicker humus layer normally develops.

Freely-drained substrata give rise to dry heathlands whereas acid soils with impeded drainage often lead to the development of wet heathland. Thicker layers of peaty humus often underlie wet heathland, and on deeper peats in high rainfall areas, *Calluna* heathland grades into cotton grass (*Eriophorum* spp) mires.

Individual soil profiles may differ considerably with respect to the nature of the parent material, degree of podsolization and iron pan development, depth of peat, presence of gleying, etc. However, most of the types of soil on which heathland is found have been described by Zehetmayr (1960), Dimbleby (1962) and Pyatt (1970).

1.6.2   The soil profile

Figure 1.2 illustrates a profile of a peaty podsol, which may be taken as broadly characteristic of relatively freely-drained upland heathland. It will serve as a reference for the description of the main soil horizons.

The upper organic layers (O horizons) contain undecayed or partly decayed plant material, forming the dark and usually fibrous mor humus (peat) which accumulates in a stratified way. The depth of peat is variable but in podzols rarely exceeds 150mm. In dry upland and lowland heaths, the organic layer is often only 25-50mm in depth. Deeper peats occur where *Calluna* heathland has developed on former sites where the peat has begun to dry out (Zehetmayr, 1960). The peat layer is the main rooting zone of the ericoid species (*Calluna* and *Erica* ssp)

Fig. 1.2. Generalised heathland soil profile.

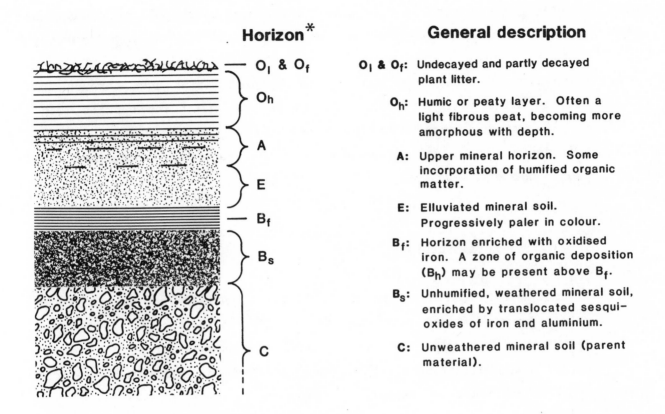

Horizon[*]	General description
O_l & O_f	O_l & O_f: Undecayed and partly decayed plant litter.
O_h	O_h: Humic or peaty layer. Often a light fibrous peat, becoming more amorphous with depth.
A	A: Upper mineral horizon. Some incorporation of humified organic matter.
E	E: Elluviated mineral soil. Progressively paler in colour.
B_f	B_f: Horizon enriched with oxidised iron. A zone of organic deposition (B_h) may be present above B_f.
B_s	B_s: Unhumified, weathered mineral soil, enriched by translocated sesqui-oxides of iron and aluminium.
C	C: Unweathered mineral soil (parent material).

[*] **Nomenclature according to Fitzpatrick, 1967.**

and many of the other heathland plants (Chapman, 1970; Gimingham 1972).

The junction between the A and E horizons is usually sharply delineated because of the absence of deep-burrowing earthworms. The E horizon is generally light brown in colour due to staining of the mineral particles with humus leached from above. With increasing depth this layer may become progressively more bleached due to mobilisation of iron, aluminium and other ions by humic acids percolating down through the profile after falls of rain. Deeper rooting heathland species (e.g. purple moor-grass, (*Molinia caerulea*) penetrate the E layer (Gimingham, 1972), and may pass through the iron deposition zone if the pan is not well developed.

1.6.3   Mineral nutrient content

In most heathland soils, the pH value is between 3.5 and 5.5, although values below 3.0 are sometimes found. The soils are generally very deficient in phosphorus, and are often nitrogen-deficient due to low rates of mineralisation of this element. Levels of exchangeable cations are relatively low in general.

Tables 1.2 and 1.3 give soil analysis data for various types of heathland. The data for the Shap and the Muggleswick Common soil horizons show changes in physico-chemical properties with soil depth. The upper horizons clearly maintain a much higher content of organic matter (measured as loss on igniton). Total nitrogen and total phosphorus are relatively closely correlated with total organic matter. Total phosphorus and calcium tend to decrease from the upper horizons to the elluviated horizons but often tend to increase again in the B horizon. This pattern is consistent with the effects of leaching and podsolization and occurs in many heathland soils.

1.6.4   The buried seed bank

When heathland is disturbed by construction work, by mineral extraction or by burning, regeneration of the vegetation will depend on buried dormant seeds in the soil, on regrowth from dormant buds, and on immigrant seed from adjacent heathland. Heathland soils contain a considerable 'bank' of buried viable seeds of the native species, and

Table 1.2   **Heathland soil profile analysis. Site A, near Shap, Cumbria**

Sample depth (mm)	Description/horizon (3 cores)	pH	% loss on ignition	N (%)	P	K	Ca
				Total levels		(µg.g⁻¹)	
0-20	Fibrous peat (Ol+Of+Oh)	3.10	82.7				
20-40	Amorphous peat (Oh)	3.00	60.2	1.02	723	725	230
40-60	Amorphous peat (Oh)	3.00	50.4				
60-80	Amorphous peat (Oh)	3.00	35.7	0.80	568	560	230
80-100	Peaty sandy loam (E)	3.00	16.3				
100-150	Peaty sandy loam (E)	3.10	14.3	0.35	293	600	195
0-20	Fibrous peat (Ol+Of+Oh)	3.10	86.9				
20-40	Sandy peat (Oh+E)	3.00	66.9	1.24	950	780	315
40-60	Sandy peaty loam (E)	3.05	29.1				
60-80	Peaty clay loam (E)	3.30	25.0	0.50	418	460	315
80-100	Silty clay + gravel (A+B)	3.60	14.6				
100-150	Silty clay + gravel (B)	3.70	8.3	0.20	350	695	475
0-20	Fibrous peat (Ol+Of+Oh)	2.95	87.2				
20-40	Sandy peat (Oh+E)	2.90	63.2	1.04	693	560	210
40-60	Peaty loam with sand (E)	2.95	24.4				
60-80	Peaty loam with sand (E)	3.00	20.4	0.42	280	375	140
80-100	Peaty loam with sand (E)	3.15	22.6				
100-150	Sandy clay with gravel (B)	3.60	8.1	0.31	327	440	375

See Fig. 1.2 for an explanation of soil profile symbols Ol,Of,Oh,A,E,B etc.

Table 1.3 **Heathland soil profile analysis, Site B, Muggleswick Common, Durham**

Sample depth (mm)	Description/horizon (3 cores)	pH	% loss on ignition	Total levels			
				N (%)	P	K	Ca
					(ug.g⁻¹)		
0–20	Litter + peat (Ol+Of+Oh)	3.40	75.1	0.60	325	300	140
20–40	Sandy peat (Oh+E)	2.85	42.9				
40–60	Peaty sand (E)	2.80	14.2	0.16	93	110	20
60–80	Silty sand + peat (E)	2.80	6.5				
80–100	Silty sand (B)	2.80	7.8	0.14	65	195	30
100–150	Sandy silt (B)	2.80	8.4				
0–20	Litter + peat (Ol+Of+Oh)	2.85	73.4	0.84	478	465	215
20–40	Sandy peat (Oh+E)	2.85	49.9				
40–60	Peaty silt (E)	2.90	39.7	0.57	350	725	375
60–80	Peaty silt (E)	2.90	39.6				
80–100	Silty sand + peat (E)	2.90	26.7	0.17	88	210	50
100–150	Silt (B)	2.95	5.4				
0–20	Litter + peat (Ol+Of+Oh)	3.10	81.5	1.22	780	635	455
20–40	Fibrous peat (Oh)	3.00	83.7				
40–60	Fibrous peat (Oh)	3.00	74.8	0.71	465	325	325
60–80	Peaty sand (E)	3.00	33.0				
80–100	Silty sand + peat (E)	3.05	21.7	0.15	150	670	455
100–150	Silty clay (B)	3.25	6.3				

See Fig. 1.2 for an explanation of soil profile symbols Ol,Of,Oh,E,B etc.

these seeds may remain viable for many years. The fauna which normally assist deep burial and redistribution of seeds through the soil profile are much less abundant in heathland soils, and therefore the seed bank is concentrated into the lower organic horizon.

This seed bank has been investigated fairly thoroughly. Miles (1973) sampled the buried seed populations of three *Calluna* dominated soils in north east Scotland. A peaty podzol contained 1360 seeds m^{-2} of *Calluna* in the top 20mm, and an iron-humus podzol contained 517 seeds m^{-2} of this species. In a brown forest soil, 1700 seeds m^{-2} of *Calluna* were found, together with seeds of 19 other species. The species composition of all seed banks correlated well with the existing vegetation at the sites.

In other work, Miles (1973, 1974) demonstrated that providing that the integrity of soil horizons remained undisturbed, the heathland vegetation could regenerate effectively from seed, even when the existing vegetation had been destroyed by physical removal.

Miles (1974) also examined the effects of removing various parts of the soil profile to determine whether this would improve the germination and establishment of deliberately introduced seed of non-native species. Removal of the litter and fermentation layers of the soil profile significantly improved the survival of introduced species (e.g. *Deschampsia flexuosa* and *Galium saxatile*). This is indirect evidence that disturbance or loss of the upper layers of the natural soil profile may allow undesirable alien species to invade heathland.

Samples of soil from heather moorlands near Shap, Cumbria and at Esclusham Common, Clwyd, were examined by Gillham (1980). Cores to a depth of 150mm were sectioned horizontally to determine distribution of dormant viable seed of the ericoid species, through the soil profile. The relative distribution of seed is shown in Figure 1.3. Clearly, buried seed is concentrated in the top of the soil profile, little being found below 40mm. At Esclusham Common, the litter layer contained a substantial proportion of the seed bank.

Following soil disturbance, certain heathland species such as bilberry (*Vaccinium myrtillus*), purple moor-grass (*Molinia caerulea*) and

Fig. 1.3. Relative distribution of heather (*Calluna* plus *Erica* spp.) seed bank through upland heathland soil profiles.

Site A: Shap, Cumbria. 3 Cores

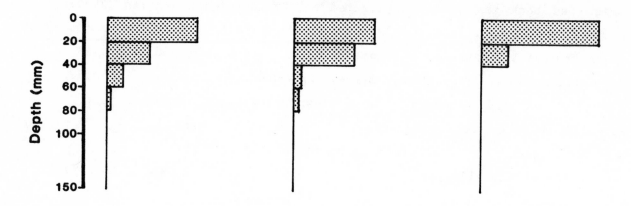

Site C: Esclusham Common, Clwyd. 3 Cores

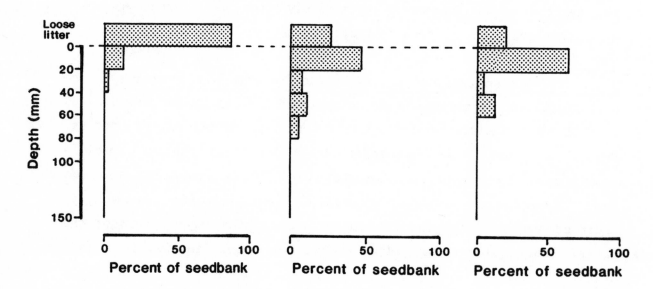

cotton grass (*Eriophorum* spp) are capable of regrowth from buried dormant buds.   This bud bank (*sensu* Harper, 1977), and the buried viable seed bank, are a most important resource which can be lost as a result of severe fire or mechanical disturbance of the upper organic soil horizons.   In most types of heathland reinstatement, preservation of the topsoil resource is essential for a successful outcome.

1.7   Germination and seedling establishment of heathers

1.7.1 Germination

Germination of seeds of *Calluna* is intermittent (Bannister, 1964; Gimingham, 1972).   Many seedlings appear in autumn after seed shedding, but a considerable proportion of seeds remain dormant, retained in their capsules until the following spring and early summer, when further germination occurs.   Seed stored dry in the laboratory may remain viable for many years.

Under artificial constant temperatures, the range 17 - 25°C appears to be most favourable for germination.   Within that range, fluctuations of a few hours' duration further increase the rate of germination and final percentage of seeds germinating.   Darkness inhibits germination, particularly at constant temperatures.   Seedlings are rarely found in shade under a dense canopy of mature *Calluna* or moorland grasses. Soil incubation experiments by Gillham (1980) showed that seedlings tended to emerge only from seed contained in the upper few millimetres of soil, and that very few seedlings emerged from seed buried deeper than 15mm.   Deep burial enforces seed dormancy.   When a heath fire removes the litter and upper humus layer, exposed seed may germinate freely.   There are indications that fire may stimulate germination if excessive temperatures do not occur.   Temperatures over 200°C are lethal, but short periods in the range 40° - 160°C could increase percent germination.   At 120°C, periods of less than 30 seconds improve germination (Whittaker & Gimingham, 1962).   Meaden (unpublished data) has shown that heat treatment of commercially supplied capsules of *Calluna* (e.g. 100°C for 30 seconds) substantially increased percent germination.

Consolidation of the substratum creates a better micro-environment for germination (Wallace, 1917; King, 1960) and seeds of *Calluna* germinate poorly on its own litter when this is fresh and loose (Gimingham 1972). Germination of *Calluna* occurs at microsites where a high humidity is maintained for several weeks, and when temperatures are suitable. Thus germination occurs mainly in autumn and spring, although in upland heathland at relatively high elevations, late spring and summer germination commonly occurs.

Bannister (1965, 1966) described the optimum conditions for the germination of *Erica cinerea* and *E. tetralix*. These are similar to those for *Calluna*, although Gillham (1980) suggests that *E. cinerea* germinates more successfully in drier soils. The proportion of *E. cinerea* seeds germinating in the course of a growing season is low (20-40%; Bannister, 1964a), although this can be substantially increased if a short heat shock is applied. Flushes of *E. cinerea* seedlings are common following heath fires (Hansen, 1964; Gimingham, 1972).

1.7.2 Seedling establishment

The establishment requirements of seedlings of ericoid species are quite exacting. The growth and survival of *Calluna* seedlings is greatly reduced if water supply in the substratum falls below field capacity (Bannister, 1964b), or if the relative humidity in the neighbourhood of the seedling is less than 60% (Gimingham, 1972). Establishment is also adversely affected by waterlogging (Whittaker & Gimingham, 1962; Gillham 1980). Seedling growth is poorer on organic than on mineral substrates but in general, highly organic soils provide a physically more suitable micro-environment for germination and establishment.

In the field, seedlings are scarce or absent where *Calluna* forms dense stands, but where there are gaps, or where areas have been disturbed, cleared or burnt, seedlings are often very numerous. The combined effects of a relatively high light intensity and protection from desiccation probably determine success of seedling establishment.

Established seedlings often occur in aggregations, presumably indicating the presence of sheltered but unshaded microsites, and are sometimes associated with the presence of mosses. Mean seedling densities varying from 2.73 per 100cm² to 87.5 per 100cm² are quoted by Gimingham (1972), but due to a patchy distribution, the effective density of established seedlings in relatively small areas (e.g. 50-200cm²) is often at the high end of the range quoted by Gimingham (author's observations). In an experiment at Lee Moor, Devon, where moorland topsoil had been stripped to a depth of 40-50mm and macerated before respreading to a depth of 25mm, Gillham (1980) recorded a mean maximum number of established ericoid seedlings of *circa* 2.0 per 100cm².

On bare and highly disturbed areas, a low density sward of slow growing grasses will often enhance seedling establishment, presumably due to maintenance of a higher relative humidity close to the soil surface. Thus, although young seedlings are sensitive to interspecific competition and excessive shading, a low density vegetation cover can be beneficial to establishment.

1.8 The developing heathland

Achieving successful seedling establishment of *Calluna* and other native moorland species is not the endpoint of the reinstatement process. In the first few months after primary reinstatement, the colonising plant community will be extremely sensitive to management practices and uncontrolled variables such as climate, which may shape the longer term species composition of the vegetation. A newly reinstated area of heathland requires positive aftercare and subsequent management.

2.0 TYPES OF DISTURBANCE TO LOWLAND HEATH AND HEATHER MOORLAND, AND ATTEMPTS TO REINSTATE THEM

2.1 Quarries and mineral extraction

2.1.1 Background

Quarrying and mineral extraction have devoured heathland in many parts of Britain for a very long time, although it is not possible to quantify losses of heathland caused by these activities. Extraction of sand and gravel inevitably impinges on heathland in many southern counties, including Devon, Dorset, Hampshire, Surrey, Sussex and Kent, and also in East Anglia, where Breckland heaths have been disturbed and damaged over a period of many years. Silica sand is extracted from lowland heathland in north Norfolk, and heathland in some Midland counties has been deleteriously affected by sand and gravel extraction.

In the south west, extraction of china clay (kaolin) in Cornwall and Devon occurs in some substantial areas of heathland. In particular, parts of Dartmoor (impinging on the National Park), Bodmin Moor and the area of granite near St. Austell have many huge open pits with adjacent heaps of coarse sand waste and mica lagoons. Heathland is destroyed mainly by the extension of waste tips. In Dorset, lowland heathland has been somewhat damaged by extraction of ball clay at Arne in the Purbeck area. There is no evidence of extensive damage to heathland caused by hard rock quarrying, although in Derbyshire, limestone heathland has been destroyed by open-cast extraction of fluorspar, and in Durham fluorspar working has damaged heathland. Limestone heathland can sometimes be at risk from dust blowing from a nearby quarry.

In Devon and Cornwall, extraction of heavy metals, particularly tin, with the associated waste rock dumps and tailings lagoons, has destroyed small areas of heathland. This could have become a more significant problem, if the minor renaissance in the mining industry in the south west had continued, but recent events suggest that mining will be reduced or will cease altogether.

2.1.2 Restoration of quarry wastes and mineral extraction sites

Successful experimental reinstatement of heather moorland has been
carried out by English China Clay International plc at one site in
Devon and two small sites in Cornwall. In Devon, the methods used were
based on work by Gillham (1980) on sand waste at Lee Moor, near
Plymouth. The approach was to utilise topsoil and litter which would be
destroyed during the quarrying and tipping operations. In section 1.6.4
it was emphasised that most heathland soils contain a substantial number
of dormant viable seeds of *Calluna, Erica* spp and some other
heathland species. This was the seed source used in the reinstatement
process.   Generally it takes about 5 years for *Calluna* seedlings to
establish and reach a reasonable degree of cover. Further details of
this type of reinstatement are presented in sections 3.2 and 3.3.

Gillham's experimental work established some ecological principles of
heathland reinstatement. Details of the work are given in Appendix I,
section 1.1, and illustrated in Plates 1-4.   A parallel practical
attempt was also made (Coppin, pers.comm. 1981) to reinstate heathland
at Blackhill Quarry, near Exmouth, Devon, on an area of approximately
two hectares. Where sand and gravel had been extracted, an area had
been graded to a gentle slope by earthmoving machinery. Litter and
topsoil were again imported as a seed source, and although early
establishment of *Calluna* was achieved, lack of management of the
establishing vegetation has led to it being subsequently over-run by
gorse. Details are in Appendix I (1.2).

English China Clay International plc attempted limited restoration of
heathland species on a small area (0.5 ha) of coarse sand waste
(containing varying amounts of overburden) near St. Austell, Cornwall.
The area was originally sown with a mixture of Highland bent (*Agrostis
castellana*), red fescue (*Festuca rubra*) and white clover
(*Trifolium repens*), and some lime and fertiliser had been applied
(amounts not known - no record). Litter was collected from adjacent
moorland and was spread by hand soon after the grasses had been sown.
The amount of litter used was not accurately recorded. After three
years, on a substrate consisting predominantly of coarse sand
waste, *Calluna* and *Erica cinerea* had established in about equal

abundance (about 15-20 individuals m⁻²), and western gorse (*Ulex gallii*) was also present in abundance. The heathers tended to occur in rows, reflecting seedling establishment *amongst* the drilled rows of grasses. This indicates the protective effects of companion grass species in a low productivity environment (section 3.6). After three years, total vegetation cover was only 30-40%. This area was seriously disturbed in 1983, and further development of heathland vegetation ceased.

In another part of the area where overburden was the main component of the substrate, there was a much higher biomass of grasses and white clover, and birdsfoot-trefoil (*Lotus corniculatus*) was also present. In these patches, the heathers occurred *between* the original drilled rows of grasses (about 2-3 individuals m⁻²), indicating the competitive effect of the grasses in supressing heather seedling establishment in a more fertile substrate.

It is emphasised that reinstatement or establishment of heathland *de novo* on bare substrates cannot normally be achieved as a single operation. Management over a period of several years will be required.

English China Clay International plc had previously shown in small experimental plots (Owen, pers. comm. 1980), that it was possible to create a heathland vegetation by spreading topsoil on a level substrate of coarse sand waste. The heathland topsoil was removed to a depth of about 150mm and respread at the same depth. After four years, in an area protected from grazing, there was >90% cover of *Calluna*, *Erica* spp, *Molinia caerulea* and other moorland grasses (Plate 5). During the first growing season, half the experimental plots had been sprayed with paraquat to remove grasses (*Molinia* in particular), which had regenerated rapidly. It was considered that these might suppress establishment of heather seedlings. However, there was ultimately no difference between the species composition in sprayed and in unsprayed sub-plots.

Success is not always guaranteed, even with the use of appropriate seed sources. The complete failure of *Calluna* to germinate was in one

case (at a silica sand quarry near Kings Lynn, Norfolk) due to the
litter being smothered with blown sand. At Rockford Common in
Hampshire, the topsoil and litter had been spread too thinly to provide
enough suitable microsites to allow establishment of *Calluna*.
Furthermore at this site, agricultural grasses were sown, probably with
the addition of fertiliser. When the fences were broken, and ponies
allowed to over- graze the area, the grasses became dominant.

2.1.3 Recommendations for reinstatement of heathland on quarry and
      mining wastes

a) It is important that quarry operators plan reinstatement procedures
    as an integral part of the extraction and restoration operations and
    not as an afterthought. Thus sources of heathland species (as seed,
    litter or heathland topsoil) must be identified and conserved.

b) Areas of heathland which are about to be destroyed by extending a
    working face or by tipping of wastes can be stripped, stored for
    periods of a few weeks and subsequently spread on bare substrates
    where reinstatement is required.

c) Even when no heathland is being made directly available by mining or
    quarrying activities, adjacent heath could be used as a donor site,
    and lightly rotovated to allow a thin layer (about 40-50mm) to be
    stripped off for use in reinstatement. The donor area of heathland
    will normally regenerate fairly rapidly.

d) Where heathland is available for stripping, existing vegetation, if
    not already fairly short, should be cut and lightly rotovated to aid
    handling and respreading. If costs have to be minimised, it may not
    be necessary to rotovate, since successful reinstatement has been
    achieved simply by stripping and replacing topsoil in lumps.
    However normally reinstatement should be improved where topsoil is
    rotovated before removal. The depth of rotovation and stripping
    should not exceed 100mm, but in any event should be adjusted to peat
    topsoil depth at a particular site.

e) Topsoil should be stored for the minimum possible period before
    spreading at a depth of about 50mm on the reinstatement site.
    Storage in excess of a few weeks will prevent vegetative
    regeneration of many native heathland species. Bilberry
    (*Vaccinium myrtillus*) may regenerate from dormant buds when
    stored moist for periods of two or three months. If the mineral
    substrate is relatively coarse, blinding with finer material may be
    beneficial, otherwise a thicker layer of heathland topsoil may be
    necessary.

f) All areas of heathland reinstatement should be protected from
    grazing by cattle, sheep, horses etc. for at least three years and
    ideally for a longer period. Five years would normally be
    sufficient.

2.2 Construction : reservoirs, containment dams, and roads

2.2.1 Associated reinstatement problems

Road embankments, verges and dam faces are generally obtrusive landscape
features that should be designed to blend with the surrounding landscape
However, there have been few serious attempts to restore the natural
vegetation where upland or lowland heaths have been affected.

Adjacent areas will often be considerably damaged by contractors'
equipment, and by the need for space for site offices, parking and
access roads. Restoration of heathland vegetation may be difficult due
to restricted availability of heathland topsoil or turves. Where a
reservoir, a tailings lagoon or a road, destroys areas of heathland
there is potential for saving and storing the soil and transplanting
turves. The practical problems will be location of soil storage sites,
avoiding undue length of soil storage, and with turves, arranging
immediate transfer from donor to recipient sites. In a large scale
construction project, the planning and design of restoration procedures
obviously needs to be considered at an early stage and in close
consultation with project engineers. It may sometimes be impossible

to reconcile requirements for restoration with the engineering construction programme.

A particular problem of construction projects involving deep peats, either at high altitude in England and Wales or at high and low altitudes in Scotland, is stabilisation of the substrate. Peats and mixed peat/subsoil materials are liable to flow when saturated with water. Containment and stabilisation of the substrate may need to be an integral part of the process of vegetation restoration.

Road embankments and verges in heathland areas often have been sown with inappropriate species of grasses and herbs, typically DoE recommended road verge seed mixtures based on perennial rye-grass. This initially produces a vegetation which emphasises the presence of the road. If sown vegetation is not maintained with later input of fertiliser, it becomes relatively moribund, and natural colonisation by native heath- land plants including *Calluna* and *Erica* spp often occurs. Typical examples are verge sections alongside the A31 road through the New Forest, although disturbance has caused colonisation by gorse (*Ulex* spp.) which may be undesirable where thickets create a fire hazard.

2.2.2 Attempts to reinstate containment dams, and areas affected by associated construction works

A Welsh Water Authority reservoir regulating the River Dee, at Llyn Brenig, Clwyd, is situated in heather moorland at an elevation of about 360m. The approach used to reinstate heather on the dam face was to transplant large turves of heather (*circa* 1.0m x 1.0m x 0.5m). These were taken from an area which was to be flooded, using large tracked diggers, and the turves were roughly placed, or rolled over the upper part of the dam face. No attempt was made to ensure that the turves rested in a vertical position or that they were placed in pits so that each turf was flush with the ground surface. The work was carried out in June 1976, soon after construction of the dam had been completed.   There was complete failure of the turves to establish, except in one relatively small area adjacent to the Water Authority offices, where the turves were regularly watered. On the dam face, the severe drought in summer 1976, combined with subsequent erosion by wind driven rain, killed existing heather plants and ensured that heather seedling establishment was very poor, since the turves progressively disintegrated.

Subsequent experimental work at Llyn Brenig (Meaden, 1983) has shown that fencing of turfed areas at that site is essential for successful establishment, since grazing by sheep rapidly destroys the heather plants even when the turf is placed in a pit flush with the ground. In Meaden's experiments, where small turves (0.5m x 0.5m x 0.25m) were placed in exclosures, survival of heather shoots was about 45% after 13 months. All the original *Calluna* shoots were dead after two years, but within the fenced area they had been replaced by seedlings. Survival may have been improved if turves had been removed from a fairly young stand of heather (e.g. 3-4 years' old), but only older heather (8-10 years) was available for Meaden's experiment.

Attempts to establish heather moorland at the Central Electricity Generating Board (CEGB) pumped storage reservoir at Marchlyn Mawr, near Llanberis, Gwynedd, have had some limited success only. During the final construction phase of the dam, conservation of topsoil and associated heather moorland vegetation (mixed as fragments with the topsoil) was apparently very poor, since the surface of the re-instated dam face consisted mainly of sub-soil materials. The very rocky terrain at this site probably caused considerable difficulties in collection and conservation of topsoil. The dam face was sown mainly with sheep's-fescue (*Festuca ovina*) and common bent-grass (*Agrostis capillaris*), which effectively prevented soil erosion at the relatively high elevation (*c.* 650m) of this site. A very few seedlings of bilberry (*Vaccinium myrtillus*) and *Calluna* have become established. Heather turves (*circa* 0.5m x 0.5m x 0.25m) were placed in pits in the dam face but subsequent survival was very poor. The site was not protected from sheep, and it is possible that poor survival resulted from sheep grazing.

In order to introduce heather at this site, *Calluna* seedlings were raised in a heated glasshouse at Bangor University's field station, Pen-y-Ffridd, using litter collected from areas of heather moorland adjacent to the dam. Heather litter was sprinkled over the surface of a sand/peat compost contained in plastic multipots and was kept moist under mist spray lines (section 3.5.1). After hardening off outdoors, three month old seedlings were planted out in irregular shaped blocks to give about 36 plants per m². Each block was fenced to protect the young heather seedlings from grazing by sheep. Over a two year period several thousand seedlings were planted. Six months after the first few batches of seedlings had been transplanted, survival was excellent. The main drawback to this approach was that it did not restore the complete heathland vegetation since other important species e.g. bilberry (*Vaccinium myrtillus*) were not included as transplants.

An attempt was made during summer 1979 to establish lowland heath vegetation on bunds (25m in height) retaining tin/copper/arsenic mine tailings at an ore processing plant near Truro in Cornwall. The method suggested by the Environmental Advisory Unit (EAU) of Liverpool University involved digging out turves from adjacent areas using a JCB, and depositing the turves over the side of the bund. No attempt was made to place the turves in particular positions or in specially dug pits. A seed mixture of companion grasses (mainly *Agrostis capillaris* and *Festuca rubra*) was hydroseeded onto part of the bund whilst another section of the bund remained unsown.

Regeneration of *Calluna* and *Ulex* spp was more effective in turves which were positioned in the grass sward, in comparison with turves on the bare substrate (Bell, pers. comm.1986). The bunds were not fenced, and there was considerable grazing by rabbits at this site. Thus, exposed turves on the bare subsoil were more severely grazed than turves in the grass sward where there was abundant alternative food for the rabbits. It is also possible that protection from exposure to desiccating winds was partly responsible for the improved regeneration in the grass sward. Recently this site has been destroyed by a major redevelopment scheme.

The CEGB undertook a feasibility study for a pumped storage power station in Longdendale, Derbyshire. The proposed location for the upper reservoir was Robinson's moss at an elevation of 500m and in an area of deep blanket peat, 3-5 metres deep. This blanket peat supports a mire or bog vegetation dominated by cotton grasses (*Eriphorum* spp), bilberry (*Vaccinium myrtillus*), wavy hair grass (*Deschampsia flexuosa*) and crowberry (*Empetrum nigrum*). However, at slightly lower altitudes and on drier slopes heather moorland is widespread. Construction work for such a project would include the dam itself, as well as access roads to the upper reservoir, with associated cuttings, embankments and bunds to contain excavated peat. Reinstatement of heather moorland would be necessary on the embankments and bunds and restoration of mire vegetation would be the objective on the surface of bunded peat. Substantial areas of bare peat substrate would be created by the construction work, and it would be necessary for rapid stabilisation of the peat surfaces, in addition to restoring the native vegetation. Natural erosion of peat is already widespread in this part of Derbyshire (Plate 6), and the techniques used are relevant to large-scale construction projects (section 2.4). The EAU is currently carrying out substantial field experiments to investigate techniques for reinstatement of the heather moorland and blanket mire vegetation at Robinson's Moss. Experiments into stabilising surfaces and introducing heather into the plant community were set up in May 1980, with larger-scale experiments established in April 1983. Details of these largely successful trials are given in Appendix I, section 2.1, and illustrated in Plates 7 - 11.

Also in Derbyshire, but at the proposed site of a new BBC transmitter at Holme Moss, larger scale restoration is being carried out (Anderson, pers.comm.1987). This site is at a similar elevation to Robinson's Moss, with similar peat and mineral substrates. An area of approximately 0.4ha was hydro-seeded in July 1984 with a grass seed and fertiliser mixture (seed at 90 kg ha^{-1}, fertiliser at 150 kg ha^{-1}). Ground or crushed limestone was also applied at a rate of 1000 kg ha^{-1}. The seed mixture contained *Festuca ovina*, *Festuca rubra* and *Agrostis castellana* (cv. Highland). In Autumn 1984, cut heather (with attached seed capsules) was spread over the area, and pushed into the ground surface.

One thousand plants of *Empetrum nigrum* and *Vaccinium myrtillus* were hand-planted. In 1987, after three growing seasons, the sown species had the following ground cover values:

Grasses	28%
Heather	11%
Mosses	24%
Bare ground	34%

A further 4.5 ha were treated in a similar way, in October 1986 and 1987, as part of a continuing programme.

2.2.3 Heathland reinstatement on roadside embankments and verges

Natural recolonisation, particularly by *Calluna*, often occurs on road verges. Thus it seems likely that deliberate reinstatement could often be successful by using appropriate sources of heathland plant material.

Experimental evidence of successful small-scale reinstatement of *Calluna* on a roadside embankment was published by Gilbert & Wathern (1976) and Wathern (1976). They showed that it was possible to establish heather on a newly-made roadside embankment where the A57 crosses heather covered millstone grit moors west of Sheffield. Heather litter was broadcast (1,250 kg ha^{-1}) on experimental plots which were simultaneously sown with seed mixtures composed of common bent-grass (*Agrostis capillaris*), red fescue (*Festuca rubra* ssp *commutata*‡ and *Festuca rubra* ssp *rubra*) and sheep's fescue (*Festuca ovina*), in various proportions (overall sowing rate 63 kg ha^{-1}). In addition, heather litter was broadcast into an adjacent sward consisting mainly of perennial rye grass (*Lolium perenne*) which had been sown on the embankment by the County Council.

During the second year after broadcasting the heather litter, there were 20 to 25 well established *Calluna* plants per m² in the slow growing grass mixtures, with the largest plants in the sward of *Agrostis capillaris*. There were no heather seedlings in the perennial ryegrass sward. After six years, well-grown bushes of *Calluna* occurred in all

‡ nomenclature according to Hubbard, 1968

plots containing the slow growing grasses, composing on average 30% of the vegetation cover.

Apart from the experimental work of Gilbert and Wathern, there have been few practical attempts to establish heathland vegetation on roadside verges, and even fewer examples where detailed records have been kept.

A successful episode of establishment of heathland vegetation *de novo* was carried out on a road embankment near Poole, Dorset in 1979. The site is an embankment to a by-pass slip road by Old Wareham Road. The approximate angle of slope is 45°. The embankment was constructed from typical motorway fill and local subsoil.

Heather turves were imported from Canford Heath (which was being developed as a housing estate) and were laid closely adjacent directly onto the subsoil and pegged into place with chestnut pegs. After five years, there was a dense and relatively even cover of *Calluna* with occasional plants of *Ulex minor* (dwarf gorse). However the species composition of the turves has changed over the five year period since, with an almost complete decline in the abundance of *Molinia caerulea* (purple moor-grass). *Molinia* is more typical of wet heath vegetation. so its decline was probably due to the site being very well-drained.

2.2.4 Recommendations

Construction sites will always tend to have a variety of heathland reinstatement requirements, whereas restoration of roadsides and embankments usually should be a more straightforward operation. Some general principles and procedures are outlined below.

a) Preliminary landscape design and planning should include an assessment of the resources for heathland reinstatement that will be available at the site or nearby. The handling of the resources will have to be integrated into engineering construction programmes.

b) In many road construction schemes, it should be possible to strip
    off and store peaty topsoil separately for subsequent replacement on
    verges and embankments. To reduce erosion on embankments,
    stabilisation using chemical stabilisers combined with sowing of
    companion grasses may be necessary.

c) For construction projects, heather litter and peaty topsoil can be
    stripped and stored before construction or site work commences in
    an area. Heather litter can be stored for long periods when
    dried. Peaty topsoil may be stockpiled for periods of several
    months. *Calluna* will effectively re-establish from seed even
    after storage, but other species which regenerate vegetatively may
    be lost.

d) On bunds and embankments, turfing may be possible. If so, this
    should be given priority because of the 'instant' landscape effect
    and continuity of the plant community.

e) On a limited scale and in areas of very high landscape sensitivity,
    it may be justifiable to use the higher cost approach of planting
    heathers grown in paper tubes. Irregular shaped patches placed in a
    grass matrix will provide seed for subsequent colonisation of the
    whole area.

2.3 Pipelines

2.3.1 Background

The number of pipelines installed for the economical transport of
natural gas, water, oil, and chemicals such as ethylene has increased
substantially in the past 20 years. Since the discovery and exploit
ation of natural gas and oil in the North Sea, the development of a gas
transmission network created a considerable increase in pipelaying
activity. The majority of offshore gas pipeline landfalls are in north
east Britain and it is inevitable that they have crossed heathland and
other semi-natural habitats. Wherever possible, there has been a pre-
ferred policy to route pipelines through farmland where techniques of

pipe installation and subsequent soil restoration have been refined to give acceptable crop yield and soil conditions. When pipelines were installed across tracts of heathland and other native upland vegetation, there was often very poor re-establishment of the original vegetation.

Until the mid-1970s, for gas pipelines being installed in northern England and southern Scotland, the usual sequence of working in heathland areas was to fence off the working width (which would be 8-30m depending on the size of the pipe), and to strip topsoil to a depth of 150-400mm across the whole of this width, stockpiling it along one side. Contractor's plant ran on the sub-soil within the working width, and materials such as sand and timber were brought in where necessary to stabilise the 'road'. The trench was excavated, and the sub-soil was stockpiled alongside the pipeline route. The pipe sections were brought in and placed alongside the trench, welded and laid into position. Finally the trench was backfilled, and the stored topsoil respread over the whole width.

A final surface was often prepared by disc harrowing the respread soil, and in some instances the ground was fertilised and seeded with pasture grasses at the request of, or directly by, the landowner or tenant farmer. After installation was completed, responsibility for the fencing generally passed to the landowner or tenant. In many cases the fencing was quickly removed (and used elsewhere), or if left, gaps were made or simply not repaired, to allow immediate access to grazing stock.

2.3.2   Reasons for poor reinstatement of heathland after pipelining

Due to the widespread practice of stripping vegetation and soil to a depth of 300-400mm across the entire pipeline easement, and the subsequent disruption of soil horizons, there has often been complete failure of reinstatement. Moffat (1973, 1975) investigated in some detail the effects of disruption by pipelines on heather moorland vegetation. Many years after pipelaying, the route may remain clearly visible as a linear landscape feature, a ribbon of vegetation clearly differentiated from the adjacent heather moorland. Moffat found that typically, the course of pipelines were characterised by areas of bare ground, the growth of sedges, rushes (*Juncus* spp) and certain coarse grass species such as mat-grass (*Nardus stricta*).

At all sites, soil conditions on the easement were considerably different from those in undisturbed heathland. Considerable changes in the physical and chemical properties of the soil occurred because of mixing of top peat with deeper peat and mineral subsoils during trench excavation and infilling, and because of churning and compaction through movement of heavy vehicles. In particular, problems of waterlogging occurred where permeability and the overall drainage characteristics of the soils were changed. Changes in the soil properties in turn affected the species composition and long-term growth of the newly colonising vegetation. Quite frequently stands of rushes developed (Plate 12), with intervening areas of bare uncolonised ground allowing surface erosion by water and wind to occur. Fig. 2.1 shows soil properties and associated vegetation in a transect across a 24 inch (610mm) gas pipeline laid in 1970 near Rothbury, Northumberland. Further details are given by Gillham & Putwain (1977); Holiday *et al.* (1979); Gillham, Putwain *et al.* (1982).

Gillham (1980) examined two gas pipeline routes through heather moorland on the Whitfield Estate, Northumberland. The depth of peat varied from 0.50 - 0.75m, and in neither case were measures taken to preserve the integrity of the top layer of peat (containing the vast majority of the viable seed bank). Mixing with mineral subsoil often occurred, and after pipelaying was completed, some mineral subsoil remained at the ground surface. At both sites, grazing by livestock occurred within a few weeks of job completion.

At the Whitfield Estate, the first pipeline was 18 inches (457mm) in diameter, laid *circa* 1970 through a mixed grass heath and heather moorland. The course of the pipeline can now be seen as a strip 2-3m wide, dominated by rushes and sedges and also containing areas of compacted clay subsoil and surface stones. The other pipeline was a 36 inch (910mm) pipe laid during 1975-76. When the easement was examined in 1979, there was a strip 25-30m in width which had been very little colonised by heather or other moorland plants (Plate 13). Peat topsoil

36

Fig. 2.1. Transect across 24 inch (610mm) gas pipeline wayleave at Rothbury, Northumberland. Vegetation and soil data.

Plant cover % of 25 samples containing greater than 50% rooted ground cover.
All other vegetation data is frequency of occurrence in 25 samples (10cm x 10cm).

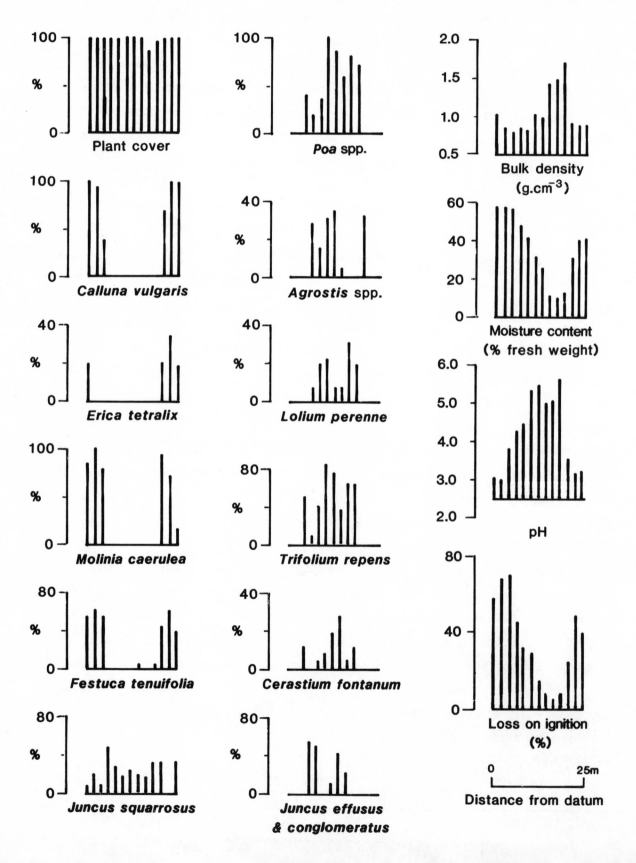

had been stripped to a depth of 150-300mm from the whole width of the easement, and had remained stockpiled for six to nine months before reinstatement. During reinstatement, much of the peat topsoil was greatly diluted and many seeds were buried at too great a depth for germination to occur. In addition, most vegetative plant parts had died because they had been buried in the soil stockpile for too long. Surface erosion, due to wetting and drying, wind, rain and frost heaving, had further restricted seedling establishment, as had grazing and trampling by sheep.

Other pipelines laid through heather moorland and acidic grassland vegetation (e.g. British Petroleum, Wilton to Grangemouth ethylene pipeline; British Gas pipeline, Rothbury, Northumberland) have been sown with an agricultural grass/clover seed mixture, and (at Rothbury at least) lime and fertiliser have been applied to the replaced soil. In both cases, fencing was removed soon after pipe installation. At Rothbury, an obtrusive bright green strip developed initially, which did not blend with the adjacent moorland landscape.

At Rothbury, colonisation by moorland plants was very restricted due to the vigorous initial growth of sown grasses. However, the original sown vegetation became much less vigorous, even moribund in some places once the supply of major plant mineral nutrients had declined (i.e. as the lime and fertiliser were leached from the soil), and once the development of bare areas and poaching by stock had become more prominent. There may eventually be slow ingress of native moorland species across the easement, but probably it will take many years to achieve a vegetation similar in character to the surrounding moorland.

Even when special precautions are taken over the restoration methods, unsatisfactory execution of the specification by the contractor can cause poor restoration of heathland. The Hankley Common (Surrey) section of the Esso aviation fuel distribution pipeline provides an example - Hankley Common is a Grade I Site of Special Scientific Interest (SSSI) where poor restoration contrasts with excellent restoration on parts of the Thursley Common National Nature Reserve (NNR). The same pipeline installation procedures were used at both sites, but during the laying of the Hankley Common section in autumn

1979, there was no special supervision, whereas there was at Thursley Common.

The specification included initial swiping of the heather which was left *in situ*, and provision for the topsoil and subsoil to be separated and placed on Terram sheeting (made from polypropylene and polyethylene) running alongside the pipe trench. Topsoil was placed on the non-working side of the pipe trench. In addition, vehicles and excavators were to run on subsoil placed on Terram sheets. The specification was very similar to that used at Hartland Moor NNR (section 2.3.3). At Hankley Common, this specification was not always adhered to, and the Terram sheet was pulled up and sections of wayleave were disturbed. Some sections were seeded with non-native grasses. Consequently there are linear grass strips running through the lowland heathland.

Other difficulties encountered at Hankley Common were organisational and structural in nature. It is claimed (Du Croz & Schofield, 1983) that despite considerable prior consultation with Esso and the consulting engineers to produce an agreed specification for the entire pipe installation operation, this was largely ignored by the contractor.

A major pipeline (910mm) was laid in 1975 between the Shell UK Ltd. oil terminal at Amlwch, Anglesey and the Shell Oil Refinery at Stanlow, Cheshire. One section of the pipeline between Llanfairfechan and the River Conway in Gwynedd passed through a grass heath rising to an altitude of c.400m. *Calluna* was not the dominant component of the vegetation, and gorse (*Ulex gallii* and *Ulex europaeus*) and bracken (*Pteridium aquilinum*) were present in some abundance. The area was well grazed by sheep and hill ponies.

During pipeline installation the topsoil was stripped from the entire working width (27.4m), and the subsoil was ripped with tines to reduce compaction. The area was sown at a low rate with slow-growing cultivars of common bent-grass (*Agrostis capillaris*), fescues (*Festuca* ssp and gorse (*Ulex europaeus*).

Although the pipeline was initially fenced, most of the fencing materials were removed by local farmers after a few months. In July

1979, four years after pipeline installation, a comparison of an area
which had remained fenced and therefore ungrazed, with the unfenced
areas showed that reinstatement of a vegetation similar to the
surrounding moorland was reasonably successful in the fenced area. In
the grazed areas, apart from a few species of bryophytes (mosses and
liverworts) and a few seedlings of *Ulex*, grass species predominated
and reinstatement was unsatisfactory. Once again, the importance of
protecting reinstated areas from grazing animals was demonstrated.

In this moorland area, the stark linear boundaries of the pipeline
easement and adjacent vegetation could have been broken up visually by
spraying immediately adjacent patches of bracken with asulam, and gorse
with triclopyr (Garlon 4) (section 4.2).

Generally, the evidence obtained from studies of pipelines shows that
ling-heather (*Calluna vulgaris*) and other heathland species such as
bell-heather (*Erica cinerea*), bilberry (*Vaccinium myrtillus*),
crowberry (*Empetrum nigrum*) etc., will not necessarily recolonise a
severely disturbed heathland soil unless special measures are taken to
preserve and return the topsoil resource with its pool of plant
propagules. These conclusions based on existing evidence, apply equally
to upland or lowland heathland.

2.3.3 Successful reinstatement of heathland over pipelines

There have been some positive and successful efforts to reinstate
heather moorland and lowland heathland after pipeline installation. The
methods used have been based on ecological principles which apply to all
kinds of heathland. The basic approach to reinstatement is to cause
minimal disturbance to the existing heathland, and the techniques which
have been developed are outlined in several articles (Gillham & Putwain,
1977; Burden, 1979;   Holliday *et al.*, 1979 and Putwain *et al.*,
1982).

During 1976, British Gas Scotland laid a ten inch pipeline over the
Pentland Hills, an area of high quality scenic and amenity value near

Edinburgh.   Soil stripping was restricted to the pipe trench only, so
that disturbance to the existing vegetation was minimised.   The depth of
strip varied between 50 and 100mm.   Terram sheets were laid adjacent to
the pipe trench for storage of topsoil, to minimise losses.   The
zonation of disturbance across the easement is shown in Fig. 2.2.
Stock-proof fencing was maintained around all areas of heather within
the easement until autumn 1983, when one section of fencing was removed,
whilst another section remains intact to the present time (1987).

After two years, there was relatively good recovery of the native
vegetation across most of the easement.   Establishment of heather was
mainly by seedlings, although in the vehicle track zone, regeneration
also occurred from buds at the base of the stems of the original heather
(*Calluna*) plants.   After five years (summer 1981), heather seedlings
had grown satisfactorily and there was a good dense monoculture of young
heather plants on the vehicle track and topsoil zones.   There were still
considerable amounts of bent grasses (*Agrostis* spp), sheep's-fescue
(*Festuca ovina*) and wavy hair-grass (*Deschampsia flexuosa*) on
some parts of the easement, with heather seedlings growing amongst the
grass tufts (Plate 14).   The pipe trench and subsoil zones had the
highest percentage of grass cover.

The visual impact of the pipeline is now greatly diminished, and where
grazing by sheep has commenced (after 7 years), grass height has been
reduced and the visual impact of the trench zone should gradually
diminish.   The effect of grazing on *Calluna* growth has been slight.

Before grazing was commenced, treatment of the grassy areas with a
growth regulator chemical or a selective herbicide (section 4.2.5) would
probably have been beneficial, to shift the balance of competition in
favour of *Calluna*.

In 1978, as part of the early development of the Wytch Farm oil fields
in Dorset, British Gas laid an eight inch oil pipeline across two short
sections of South Middlebere Heath on the Hartland Moor NNR.   Excellent

Fig. 2.2. Transect across pipeline easement, Pentland Hills near Edinburgh.

Zones of disturbance across the easement

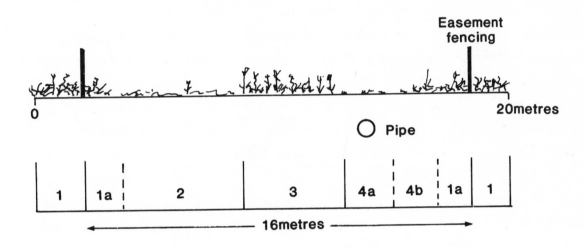

Zone	Cause of disturbance	Immediate effects
1	Undisturbed heathland	None
1a	Occasional vehicle passes.	Minor damage to standing vegetation.
2	Vehicle track; many passes by construction vehicles.	Complete defoliation of standing vegetation. Some consolidation of soil.
3	Stockpiling of topsoil from above pipe trench. Laying out and welding of pipe sections.	Variable degree of damage to standing vegetation. Soil undisturbed.
4a	Excavation of pipe trench.	Standing vegetation destroyed. Soil profile disturbed.
4b	Stockpiling of subsoil from pipe trench.	Damage to standing vegetation and soil surface during backfilling. Contamination with surplus subsoil from trench.

restoration of this lowland heath has been achieved (Burden, 1979) (Plate 5). The method recommended by Burden was similar to that suggested by Gillham & Putwain (1977) for the Pentland Hills gas pipeline, except that vehicles ran on a specially constructed sand road which rested on Terram sheets (Figure 2.3). Fuller details of the method are given by Tuck (1979).

For each section on the Hartland Moor NNR, the whole operation of trench excavation, pipe stringing, installation and trench refilling, plus laying and removal of the sand road, was completed in two days. There was minimal damage to the existing heathland vegetation. An inspection was made after one year, and at that time the main area of damage was restricted to the 1.5m wide pipe trench zone. Adjacent to the pipe in the position of the sand road and the soil stockpile, heather was flattened but not seriously damaged. The percent cover of heathland in these zones varied from 30 - 55% with additional cover provided by bryophytes. When examined again only two years and four months after installation regrowth of *Calluna* and *Erica* spp was excellent (Plate 15). Vegetative regrowth had occurred in many plants which had been covered by the sand road, and many new seedlings had emerged.

In 1983, more than four years after installation, the EAU carried out a survey of the restoration for BP International Ltd and concluded that:

   i)   the installation of the pipeline had caused little disturbance to the vegetation and the soil profile,

   ii)   restoration of the heath vegetation was excellent, with no obvious change in species composition, and total percent vegetation cover mainly above 90% and often above 95%,

   iii) the use of Terram sheet was invaluable in preventing damage to vegetation and preventing soil mixing,

   iv)   liaison with the Nature Conservancy Council Reserve Warden, and his constant presence during the laying of the pipe ensured that specifications were adhered to by the contractor.

Fig. 2.3. Minimal disturbance methods of pipeline installation.

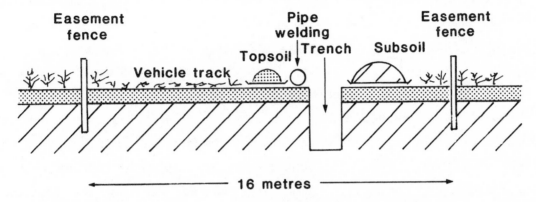

a) Method used in Pentland Hills, showing soil placement, trench position, etc.

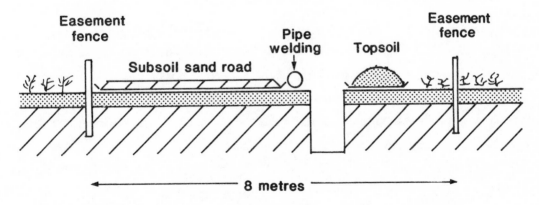

b) Method used in lowland heath (Hartland Moor NNR) Dorset, after Burden (1979).

Other attempts at reinstatement of lowland heathland after pipeline installation have met with limited success. For example, a pipeline diversion was laid near the Furzebrook rail terminal, Wareham, Dorset at a location close to the oil pipeline previously described, and on similar heathland. The specification was advised by Coppin (pers. comm.1981) and the procedures were as follows. First, a 10m wide strip of the existing heather was mown with a rotary scythe (50mm minimum height). A seven metre working width was then rotovated (4 to 6 passes by a tractor-mounted rotovator) to a depth of 100-150mm, and this was removed (by a tracked digger) and stored on polythene sheets. The next 10mm layer was removed and stored separately, and the two layers were ultimately replaced in reverse order. The storage area was a 3m wide strip additional to and adjacent to the working area. Heavy rain and manouvering by the stripping machine caused churning and mixing of topsoil and subsoil. After three years there was relatively poor recolonisation by heather species, although some other native heathland species (e.g. *Molinia caerulea*) had established a good vegetation cover. A more recent examination of this area in 1984 did not indicate any new colonisation by *Calluna* or *Erica* spp. Although the comparisons are limited, it would appear that the minimal disturbance approach to pipeline installation provides the best potential for successful reinstatement of lowland heathland and heather moorland.

In 1979, using a method similar to that successfully used in the Pentland Hills, British Gas North Eastern laid a 6 inch diameter pipeline across the North York Moors from Whitby to Pickering. A survey showed that in 6 years, nearly 80% of this pipeline route had virtually recovered and was difficult to see. In contrast there was only 20% recovery in 16 years along most of the moorland route of a 30 inch transmission main also laid across the moors in 1970 using traditional total strip methods. Interestingly, in one section of the 1970 pipeline, only the trench was stripped, and the pipe-laying machinery ran directly on the vegetation. Recovery in this particular section has consequently been very good.

2.3.4 Recommendations

The basic recommendations given below are equally appropriate for lowland and upland heaths (except those on deep peats). However, each pipeline project will have its own engineering and restoration problems, which will depend on the size of the pipe and site characteristics such as topography and drainage, soil type, vegetation type and its condition, time of the year when the work is carried out, etc.

a) Preparation of site prior to pipelaying

Before installation work commences, the route through the heathland area should be surveyed in order to map plant communities, to designate any potential problem areas, to examine the soil profile at intervals on the pipe route, and to collect soil and litter samples where necessary for testing for content of plant propagules.

The easement should be reduced to the minimum width compatible with the practical requirements of pipeline installation. The minimal disturbance approach normally requires a narrower easement since less space is required for soil storage.

b) Special precautions during the pipelaying operation

It should not normally be necessary to strip peat topsoil from the whole of the working area of the easement, as this would almost certainly reduce the chances of successful heather regrowth.

Peat topsoil should be removed only from the pipe trench and only to a depth of 100 - 150mm if practicable, since this is the seed rich layer. It should not be diluted by lower soil horizons containing little or no seed.

Geotextile sheeting (e.g. Terram) should be used for separate storage of peat topsoil and subsoil.

Problems of soil churning and compaction will be reduced if pipelaying is carried out during the summer. The success of restoration of heathland is usually reduced if pipe installation is carried out in water-logged soils.

On dry lowland heaths in particular, existing heather may be protected by construction of a sand or ballast road on geotextile sheet.

When installing smaller diameter pipe, it should be possible to dig the trench with one pass of the machinery and backfill with a second pass, with all other movements of machinery and vehicles restricted to the sand road or vehicle track.

c) Reinstatement and aftercare

If the main recommendations are carried out, then heather regeneration should take care of itself and a satisfactory heather cover should usually be achieved after four or five growing seasons.

It is essential that stock-proof fencing should be maintained along the easement boundary for four or five years at least, because trampling, poaching and grazing of young heather by sheep or other stock will severely retard heather establishment and regrowth.

On common land in upland areas, maintenance of fencing may be difficult, if not impossible. However it may be possible by means of management agreements with farmers who have grazing rights, to arrange to retain temporary fencing for three of four years, which will greatly assist reinstatement of the heathland vegetation.

Severely churned areas or where subsoil has been left at the surface may benefit from a supplementary application of seed in the form of litter or peat topsoil collected from adjacent areas of heathland. On steeper slopes where soil erosion may be a problem, it may be necessary to sow a mixture of slow-growing companion grass species.

2.4 Reinstatement of naturally eroded peat, trampled areas, and other bare substrates

2.4.1 Background

Lowland heaths are particularly suspectible to vegetation die-back, and to subsequent erosion due to trampling by visitors on foot, horseback or motorcycles.   Lowland heaths are common as recreation environments in south-east Britain, in the Midlands and in parts of the north-west where sandstone occurs.   These heaths survived as common land or as unworked areas in great estates and thus became available to public access.

Restoration problems sometimes involve substantial bare areas, but more often arise from ever-widening footpaths and a transition from *Calluna/ Erica* heath to grass-dominated heath.   Generally, there have been few serious attempts to restore bare eroded areas to lowland heath. Restoration objectives have formed part of broader management programmes designed to reduce encroachment by gorse, bracken, birch etc., and where local severe fires have occurred.   The National Trust appears to have led the way in using this approach in Surrey and Sussex.

In upland areas, particularly in the Pennines, erosion damage to heather moorland is widespread.   Most of this is 'natural', i.e. unexplained, but is exacerbated by excessive sheep stocking (Tallis & Yalden, 1983).

Detailed studies of peat erosion in the Peak District National Park (Table 2.1) showed that footpath erosion is of widespread occurrence in upland areas, and the visual effect can be obtrusive due to the linear scar.   In general, the reinstatement of footpaths to heather moorland vegetation has been on a small scale, although the Yorkshire Dales National Park initiated a major piece of work in 1986 (Bayfield & McGowan,1986;   Bayfield & Miller,1986).

Table 2.1   **Approximate extent (ha) of eroding ground in the Peak Park, 1979.**   (after Tallis, 1982).

Gullied peat	1,000 - 2,000
Marginal peat erosion	50
Accidental burns	500 - 600
Footpath erosion	50
Hillcrest erosion	750 - 950

To a considerable extent, the practical reinstatement methods of coping with this kind of problem are similar to those where there has been heavy construction work, or where severe fire has killed existing vegetation and also the seed and bud bank over a large area.

2.4.2   Restoration of trampled and eroded areas

The major recent work on upland heather moor has been carried out by a
small team from Manchester University aided by two field specialists.
The work was administered by the Peak Park Joint Planning Board, and a
detailed report was published in 1983 (Tallis & Yalden, 1983).

The objectives were to test simple experimental methods which would
achieve revegetation of heather moorland in existing eroded areas of
bare peat and mineral soils.   There were six experimental sites of
differing substrates, at altitudes ranging from 420m to 520m (Table
2.2).   The following experimental treatments were established in
December 1979:

  a) addition of cut heather bearing seed capsules at a rate of 5 kg
      (wet weight) per 4m x 4m plot,

  b) fencing to prevent grazing, or none,

  c) addition of larch forestry brashings (branches), or Bitumuls
      stabiliser, or none.

The results over three growing seasons indicated that:

  a) Fencing to keep sheep out was essential. On unenclosed treated
      areas, seedling survival was very low and flowering of
      established plants was greatly reduced.

  b) Increase in *Calluna* cover was generally greater on the lower
      altitude sites on mineral rubble, or on mixed peat and mineral
      rubble.

  c) Addition of cut heather with seed capsules was necessary.
      Fencing without input of *Calluna* seed gave a very slow
      increase in vegetation cover.

  d) Stabilisation of the surface using larch branches or Bitumuls,
      then adding seed as cut heather gave greater *Calluna* percent
      cover than addition of cut heather alone.

Table 2.2.   Peak District Moorland Restoration Project,
                characteristics of the experimental sites

Site	Altitude	Grid ref.	Substrate	Former vegetation	Date when set up
Burbage Moor	420	SK 280832	Mineral rubble	Heather moor on shallow peat	March 1980
Cabin Clough	430	SK 074927	Patchwork of peat and mineral	Heather moor on deeper peat	March 1980
Doctor's Gate	490	SK 096933	Peat and mineral	Still part vegetated, varied	Feb 1980
Holme Moss SW	510	SE 092040	Mineral soil and rubble	*Deschampsia* grassland	July 1980
Holme Moss NE	520	SE 094046	Peat	Blanket bog on deep peat	March 1980
Holme Moss NE	520	SE 093047	Mineral rubble	Blanket bog on deep peat	March 1980

Because the sites were very heterogeneous with respect to substrate, topography, aspect, etc., there was great variation between replicated treatment plots.

At the highest site (Holme Moss), where there is severe exposure and high substrate instability, the treatments failed completely on peat, failed badly on one mineral substrate, and performed poorly on another mineral rubble.

Having seen the successful EAU experiments at Robinson's Moss, (section 2.2.2 and Appendix I, section 2.1) the Peak Park study team used a similar approach to establish moorland vegetation on peat at Holme Moss. It was confirmed that input of mineral nutrients, ground limestone and a sown companion grass was required to obtain development of native species including *Calluna*.

The National Trust have also started moderate scale restoration in the Peak District National Park in the vicinity of Kinder Scout. The approach has been very practical and low-cost. There is an ongoing restoration programme which commenced in 1983. A four hectare experimental area was established at Kinder Low. Half of the area was fenced. Heather stems about 8" (20cm) long, were cut from surrounding moorland in September or October, and spread on to the bare peat, then notched in with a boot-heel. To date, one ton of cut heather has been notched into the bare peat. It is still too early to assess the success of the approach, but 'hundreds of small heather seedlings are visible'. (National Trust, 1986).

At lowland heath sites, erosion is generally not 'natural'. At Frensham Common Country Park, erosion damage (largely caused by parked cars) had become widespread with a bare area of 2.8 ha adjacent to Frensham Great Pond, another eroded area of 1.4 ha and various eroded tracks. The bare coarse sand substrates were derived from degraded iron-humus podsols.

The main site at Frensham was prepared for hydraulic seeding by discing-in dry straw at a rate of 1.5 tons/acre. The area was hydroseeded with a grass/legume mixture but no attempt was made to include heather seed or litter. The slurry also contained wood cellulose fibre, inorganic fertiliser (10% N, 15% P_2O_5, 10% K_2O), seaweed extract and poultry manure extract. The other areas were sown (not hydroseeded) with a similar mixture and fertilised, although no details are available. All sites were fenced.

The significance of this attempt at restoration is that after three years, *Calluna* had started to colonise the grass sward on the main area with a percent cover value of 0.5%, whilst the two restored tracks had higher values of 9% and 24%. After six years, the tracks had >70% *Calluna* cover. Since there was unlikely to have been any existing *Calluna* seed pool in the eroded areas, the colonising plants must have arisen from blown seed. Linear bare areas, such as eroded tracks or pipeline routes, will become colonised more rapidly than large blocks of bare substrate because the sources of colonising propagules are close by. Natural colonisation is unpredictable and it would be very risky to allow a restoration programme to be governed by the vagaries of nature.

A situation which is different but also relevant is where there has been extensive bracken control on lowland heaths. Investigations in East Anglia (Lowday, 1984 a,b) have indicated that after removal of bracken *Calluna* can be reinstated, providing that residual loose litter is removed. In 1978, Lowday established an experiment at Cavenham Heath, Suffolk, to test litter dispersal treatments after bracken had been killed by spraying with asulam. There were four main-plot litter dispersal treatments:

    a) untreated
    b) burnt
    c) raked off
    d) rotovated

Each plot was split, with one half left untreated and the other half with an addition of 20,000 *Calluna* seeds m^{-2} (collected locally). The results for the 1981-1983 period are shown in Table 2.3 (Lowday, 1984 b).

Table 2.3   The effects of litter dispersal (main treatment n=8) and
              seeding with *Calluna* (sub treatment n=4) on the % cover
              of *Calluna*, Cavenham Heath, 1981-1983 (from Lowday 1984b)

Litter dispersal	(a) Main treatment			(b) Sub treatment			
	1981	1982	1983		1981	1982	1983
Untreated	0.5	2.0	5.5	unseeded	0.1	0.3	0.9
				seeded	0.9	3.7	10.1
Burnt	2.5	8.8	16.4	unseeded	0.1	1.5	3.8
				seeded	4.9	16.1	29.0
Litter removed	9.4	21.3	36.5	unseeded	0.3	1.7	4.6
				seeded	18.5	40.9	68.4
Rotovated	7.9	21.1	28.4	unseeded	0.5	1.7	5.5
				seeded	15.3	40.5	51.3
LSD ($p < 0.05$)	5.6	5.8	10.6	LSD ($p < 0.05$) between any two sub-treatments	7.4	8.7	16.0

It was clear that deliberate input of *Calluna* seed was crucial for restoration of the heathland. Unseeded plots had a very slow rate of *Calluna* colonisation. It was also clear that removal of loose litter was essential. Raking off the litter gave the greatest percent cover of *Calluna*, but rotovation was also effective. Other native heathland species also colonised the bare experimental area, including abundant birch seedlings. It appears that further management will be required to ensure that birch does not dominate the restored plots.

2.4.3 Recommendations

The diverse nature of substrates, substantial range of climatic environments, varying topography and varying severity of erosion ensures that simple restoration prescriptions are not easily applied. Each restoration programme has to be designed with the particular characteristics of the site dictating the prescription.

The general approaches that are necessary for successful restoration appear to be:

a) Provision of *Calluna* seed as harvested fruits (cut heather), as litter, or as topsoil. A wider range of heathland species will be introduced if topsoil is used.

b) Stabilisation of eroding surfaces to assist seedling establishment. This might involve laying down forestry brashings or sowing companion grass species. Use of chemical stabilisers is questionable.

c) Removal of loose litter of *Calluna* and *Pteridium aquilinum* where it is present.

d) Appropriate input of mineral nutrients. On some relatively more fertile soils, input may be quite low.

2.5 Reinstatement of severely burnt sites

2.5.1 The problems

Wildfire is a frequent and widespread cause of damage to heather
moorland in Britain. Accidental or deliberate fires, or occasional
rotational burns which become uncontrolled, sometimes ignite surface
litter and upper layers of peat. In longer burning fires, burning can
be so severe that underlying mineral soil horizons are exposed. Since
all existing heather vegetation and root rhizomes and shoot bases of
other heathland species and seed reserves are lost, regeneration of
heather on such burnt areas may be very slow. It may require two or
three decades or even longer for a heather cover to fully re-establish.
In the North York Moors National Park, for example, there is an area
which was severely damaged by fire in 1913 which has still not been
naturally restored to a stand of heather vegetation. In the Peak
District, Pike Low which was burnt in 1939 still has extensive areas of
bare peat and exposed mineral soil.

In recent decades, the generally reduced frequency of rotational
moor-burning in upland areas has resulted in increased areas of older
heather, and consequently a larger biomass of dead flammable plant
material. This has increased both the risk of wildfire and the
possibility of more severe longer-burning fires.

The character of severely fire-damaged peat surfaces varies, but erosion
is often an associated problem. In some areas, the residual peat is
charred and cracked, leading to physical loss of peat by wind erosion
and surface run-off of rainfall. Gulley formation and dissection of the
peat surface is sometimes a consequence of severe fire. Erosion often
prevents any possibility of natural colonisation by heather, even after
the passage of several decades.

In severely burnt sites, practical restoration of heathland is an
absolute necessity if the landscape is to be returned to its former
character. The restoration problem is similar to situations where
establishment of heathland is required on bare areas.

Another important consequence of severe fire in heathland is loss of plant mineral nutrients (Gimingham 1972), as the mineral elements are released during combustion of plant material. Nitrogen in particular is volatilised, and is lost as smoke. Other elements are rapidly leached from the soil or are blown away with the ash. Thus replacement of lost mineral nutrients may be necessary for reinstatement.

One other consequence of uncontrolled fire which creates a need or reinstatement or recuperative management of heathland is colonisation by trees and shrubs. Burning of heathland, particularly uncontrolled fire, tends to encourage colonisation by trees such as birch (*Betula pendula* and *B.pubescens*), and Scots pine (*Pinus sylvestris*), or by gorse (*Ulex* spp.) and bracken (*Pteridium aquilinum*). This is particularly so for lowland heath. In heather moorland, the spread of bracken is often encouraged by burning, and where there is heavy grazing, moorland grasses become a more frequent (and sometimes dominant) component of the vegetation. Although reinstatement of heather may be the first step in converting tree and shrub invaded areas back to heathland, long-term management of colonising species will be necessary in fire-damaged heaths.

2.5.2 Experimental studies

Although there have been several descriptive studies of the natural regeneration and the development of heathland vegetation after fire, there have been only a few practical attempts to reinstate heathland after severe burning. Some experimental research is in progress, and these investigations provide interim guidelines on possible reinstatement techniques.

On the North York Moors National Park, there is a co-ordinated programme of research being carried out. This has been described in two reports published in 1980 and 1986 by the National Park Committee.

At Glaisdale Moor, field trials were established in 1979 on severely fire damaged peat and on areas of eroding mineral substrates. On the burnt deep peat areas, different surface treatments are being assessed in order to test various hypotheses for explaining why establishment of heathland vegetation should be limited.

	Hypothesis	*Treatment*
A	lack of seed	none
B	presence of surface carbonised crust preventing seedlings from rooting (plus factor A)	crust stripped off
C	inadequate aeration and shelter for seedlings (plus factors A & B)	surface rotovated and rolled to compact it
D	insufficient available nutrients (plus factors A,B and C)	surface rotovated, rolled and fertilised (50kg ha^{-1} each of nitrogen, phosphorus and potassium
E	sheep grazing	area fenced

Stripping of the surface crust was done by hand raking, and the surface was cultivated using a hand rotary cultivator. Fertiliser was broadcast by hand and raked into the surface.

Other experimental treatments included:

- introduction of blocks of mature or young heather to act as colonisation foci.

- addition of materials to reduce wind exposure and desiccation in order to improve germination and establishment of heather seedlings.

Plate 1. Heather moorland restoration experiment on china clay
sand waste at Lee Moor in Devon, April 1976. Topsoil
spread (25 - 30 mm deep) directly onto sand waste or
onto a subsoil layer placed in strips, 100mm in depth.

Plate 2. Lee Moor, Devon in September 1983, showing development
of heathland vegetation directly on the sand waste, or
on the subsoil treatment. Note that *Agrostis curtisii*
is most abundant on the subsoil treatment.

Plate 3. Lee Moor, Devon in September 1983 : development of
mixed heathland vegetation directly on sand waste,
with sown *Agrostis castellana* companion grass
treatment, and high initial fertiliser input.

Plate 4. Lee Moor, Devon in September 1983 : a control treatment
on sand waste, with no sown companion grass, and zero
fertiliser input.

Plate 5. Regeneration of heathland vegetation four years after spreading topsoil to a depth of 150mm over china clay sand waste at Maggie Pie, St. Stevens, Cornwall.(ECCI plc).

Plate 6. Robinson's Moss, Longdendale, in Derbyshire : blanket mire vegetation with extensive areas of eroded peat.

Plate 7. Robinson's Moss, May 1980 : wet peat substrate with
various experimental treatments including addition
of fertiliser and ground limestone, and placement of
macerated vegetation plus the top 100mm of peat.

Plate 8. The site depicted in Plate 7, eighteen months after the
start of the experiment, showing excellent establishment
of *Deschampsia flexuosa* and *Agrostis castellana* on
plots with added fertiliser and ground limestone.

- broadcasting by hand, and rolling-in seeds of various species including: *Calluna vulgaris* (as capsules), *Betula pubescens*, (birch), *Agrostis capillaris* var. Saboval, *Festuca ovina*, *Festuca rubra* cv. S59, *Poa pratensis* and a mixture of 25% *Agrostis capillaris*, 15% *Festuca rubra*, 25% *Deschampsia flexuosa*, 10% *Holcus lanatus*, 25% *Lotus corniculatus*. Seeding rates were 15 kg ha^{-1} for *Calluna* and the grass species, and 5 kg ha^{-1} for the birch seed. In another experiment, wild oat (*Avena fatua*) was sown as a nurse species. It is effective in reducing surface erosion for at least one year, because the dead plants remain *in situ* for several months.

After twelve months there were no clear-cut results. There was considerable germination and establishment of *Calluna* seedlings amongst the stands of wild oat, but in the other treatments, there was only a very low density of heather seedlings, with no clear indication of differences between treatments.

More recent work has involved fencing areas of mainly bare peat, several hectares in extent. These areas were treated with ground limestone and inorganic fertiliser, and *Deschampsia flexuosa* and *Agrostis capillaris* were established as companion/nurse species. Heather shoots bearing seed capsules were collected in October using a forage harvester and then baled. The heather was hand-spread over the seeded areas from a vehicle exerting only low ground pressure. Results after three growing seasons have been generally promising, demonstrating the effectiveness of stock control by fencing. Grasses had established successfully, and a moderate density of heather seedlings had appeared.

At Cannock Chase (Milford Common) about 100 ha of *Calluna* heathland were severely burnt during 1976. Up to 8cm of the peaty topsoil was destroyed and surface erosion and gulleying were extensive after heavy rain in the autumn. Severely burnt areas were sown with a mixture of wavy hair-grass (*Deschampsia flexuosa*), Highland bent (*Agrostis castellana*) and creeping red fescue (*Festuca rubra*) at rates varying between 125 and 132 kg ha^{-1}. The grass seed was lightly harrowed in. No lime or fertiliser was added. Heather litter and topsoil, collected from a flailed area of old heather, were distributed over the sown areas in March 1977. After two years, where grass cover was 51-60%, the density of established heather seedlings was very low at around 1.5 m^{-2}. Where grass cover was 81-90%, the density of heather seedlings was only 0.2 m^{-2}. After four years, the area had become dominated by wavy hair-grass, with some purple moor-grass (*Molinia caerulea*) in damper areas. The density of established heather plants remained very low. Suppression of grass growth using growth retardants or herbicides would be a way of assisting further establishment of heather.

Techniques of introducing heather into severely burnt areas were further examined in 1977 by Daniels (pers.comm.1983). Mixtures of various grass species including wavy hair-grass (*Deschampsia flexuosa*), Highland bent (*Agrostis castellana*), creeping red fescue (*Festuca rubra*) and purple moor-grass (*Molinia caerulea*) were sown at several densities (31.25 kg ha^{-1} to 125 kg ha^{-1}), with and without crushed limestone and fertiliser. Mixtures of heather litter and peaty topsoil were collected from a 28 year old unburnt area of heather which had been flail mown. This material was then broadcast into the grass swards at a rate of 500 cm^3 m^{-2} (fresh material).

In other experiments, litter was collected from stands of heather varying in age from 2 years to 28 years and spread onto the original burnt areas which have been previously described and which had become dominated by grass.

After two years, where the seeding rates of the various grass species mixtures were 62.5 and 125 kg ha^{-1}, there were approximately between 40 and 100 heather seedlings per m^2. There was considerable variation in numbers between treatment plots, and some untreated (control) areas contained heather seedlings, so it was difficult to assess the effects of the treatments.

In North Wales, within the Moel Famau Country Park in the Clwydian Hills, an area of 40 ha was accidentally burnt in 1974, with a 4 ha area being a very severe burn. *Calluna* has not regenerated on this area, except for a few well grazed small plants. Apart from excellent growth of mosses (*Campylopus pyriformis*), and some regeneration of bilberry (*Vaccinium myrtillus*), vegetation cover remains very sparse, although since 1983 there has been improved regeneration in some parts. Soil erosion has occurred on exposed western/north western facing slopes, and erosion is becoming more extensive with development of gullies and rills.

Experimental work by Meaden (1983) was intended to test the extent to which loss of heather seed, loss of mineral nutrients and over-intensive grazing by sheep are factors preventing regeneration of *Calluna*. The main experimental treatments were:

a) addition of heather litter collected locally (application rate 1,250 kg ha^{-1} fresh litter)

b) sowing a mixture of companion grass species (40% *Agrostis castellana*, 25% *Agrostis vinealis*, 25% *Festuca ovina* and 10% *Deschampsia flexuosa* by weight). Sowing rate was 20 kg ha^{-1}.

c) addition of fertiliser, ICI No. 5, (17:17:17), at a rate of 150 kg ha^{-1}.

d) fencing to exclude grazing by sheep.

Results indicated that protection from grazing was essential if growth of established heather seedlings and establishment of additional seedlings was to occur successfully. Growth of *Calluna* within exclosure plots was rapid, and a few plants flowered in the first growing season. In the following years flowering was prolific. There was no measurable effect of addition of mineral nutrients, and establishment of companion grass species was not very successful, apart from *Agrostis castellana*. This may have been due to an over-cautious approach, with no crushed limestone being used, or it could have resulted from seed being blown away or removed by surface erosion. (Plate 16).

2.5.3   Recommendations

Experimental studies of reinstatement of heather moorland and lowland heath provide useful indications as to which approaches are most likely to prove successful. These are as follows:

a)   Where burning has been severe, prevention of soil erosion may be a first priority to stop loss of any remaining peaty topsoil which may still contain viable seed of native species, and to prevent exposure of mineral soil horizons which will be a physically less favourable substrate for reinstatement of heathland.

b)   To prevent erosion it will normally be necessary to sow a mixture of grass species which are appropriate to the local area, together with an application of fertiliser. The species may include wavy hair-grass (*Deschampsia flexuosa*), sheep's fescue (*Festuca ovina*), common bent-grass (*Agrostis capillaris*), brown bent grass (*Agrostis vinealis*). In some situations it may be useful to include *Agrostis castellana*, which is not a native species (Section 3.6.2).

c)   Establishment of grasses and subsequent establishment of heather seedlings may be assisted by breaking up the surface carbonised crust where it occurs. This may be achieved by using a tined cultivator, disc harrow or by shallow rotovation. Care must be taken not to cultivate too deeply or further soil erosion may be activated. After application of grass seed and heather litter/topsoil it will often be necessary to roll and compact the cultivated areas to assist establishment of seedlings, particularly of heathers.

d)   In order to replace seed and vegetative propagules of native species killed by the fire, it will usually be necessary to broadcast peaty topsoil collected from adjacent unburnt heathland. Ideally, the donor site should be an area of medium aged heather (10-20 years), which should be flail mown, then rotovated to a depth of 40-50mm.

e)   An alternative to spreading topsoil is to collect heather litter, or
     to harvest ripe seed capsules by cutting heather in October and
     November. This is less disruptive to heathland and provides a source
     of seeds but not of regenerative vegetative fragments. Litter or
     capsules can be broadcast onto a burnt area either when companion
     grass species are sown, or into a recently established grass sward.

f)   Protection from grazing animals by fencing will be absolutely
     essential unless stocking density is very low, or unless grazing
     animals such as sheep, horses etc. are absent from the area.
     Maintenance of fencing for 3 or 4 years will be necessary. There is
     no doubt that it would be unwise to attempt an expensive programme
     of re-instatement of severely burnt heathland on common or tenanted
     land, unless interested parties can reach a binding agreement on
     maintenance of fencing for several years, or on reduction in
     stocking density to a very low level.

2.6 <u>Summary of the factors affecting restoration of heathland</u>

2.6.1 Ecological factors

Successful restoration can be achieved when the fundamental ecological
requirements for germination and successful establishment of ericoid
species and other native heathland species have been satisfied. This
must be combined with maintenance of a continuing favourable environment
for growth of the heathland species.

With particular reference to *Calluna* and *Erica* spp the following
ecological factors appear to be significant.

a)   Surface erosion is a major problem. Thus substrates must be made
     as stable as possible so that erosion is minimised. Various
     technical solutions have been tested. Establishment of companion
     grass species (e.g.*Deschampsia flexuosa*) at low population
     densities has proved successful. Forestry brashings laid on
     exposed surfaces, and heeled-in cut heather shoots, have assisted
     Calluna seedling establishment. Sowing of wild oat or barley

has proved useful, since the dead stubble continues to provide stabilisation after the first growing season. Chemical stabilisers appear to have been less effective. Jute netting (which eventually degrades) may be useful for smaller areas. This was tested in 1986 at Povington Heath in Dorset on restored areas of lowland, dry and humid heath.

b) Closely related to the erosion factor is provision of microsites which provide an environment suitable for the germination and establishment of ericoid and other native species. The microsites must provide shelter, where humidity remains relatively high for extended periods. The technical solutions to the erosion problem also provide suitable microsites. One potential difficulty where grass companion species are sown is that if the sowing rate is too high, or if the substrate is too well supplied with mineral nutrients, then excessive competition from the grasses will reduce heather establishment.

c) The nature of the substrate is significant. Germination of ericoid species is poor or even zero on loose substrates with excessive litter. Thus substrates must be cleared of excessive litter and compacted moderately. Establishment of *Calluna* and *Erica* spp is usually more successful on organic (peaty) substrates, but there is good evidence that these species will colonise mineral substrates, given sufficient time.

d) Any form of mechanical disturbance, including trampling by animals or grazing, is highly deleterious to newly restored areas of heathland. Young heather plants are easily damaged, easily pulled out of the ground and are susceptible to desiccation. Thus in the early stages of colonisation and development, protection from disturbance is essential. Ideally grazing should be prevented for at least four or five years. The length of time depends partly on stocking rates and seasonal intensities, and could be adjusted accordingly.

e)   A good source of propagules of appropriate species is essential for heathland restoration.   Although establishment of *Calluna* and *Erica* spp. may be considered to be the priority in most situations, a common objective will be restoration of a heath vegetation consisting of a characteristic mixture of species in appropriate abundance.   Cut shoots of heather provides a low-cost method of establishing the dominant species.   This may be satisfactory for initial restoration of upland heather moor, but will be less suitable for restoration of the generally more diverse lowland heath.   Use of heather litter will be an improvement, since this will contain a dormant seed population of a wider range of species.   However, there is no doubt that stripping of heath topsoil from a donor site, and transferring it rapidly will provide the most successful restoration of heathland vegetation, in *ecological* terms, unless turfing is possible.   Complete restoration of heathland vegetation can be achieved by moving turves from areas which will be destroyed to areas where restoration is required.   This approach provides immediate continuity of the plant community.   Timing of the operation to autumn or milder winter periods, rapid collection and transfer of turves and careful placement at the recipient site are critical to the success of turf transfer.

f)   Whether or not addition of mineral nutrients will be beneficial or deleterious to any particular heathland restoration situation will depend on the properties of the substrate.   Some substrates such as deep acid upland peats or silica mineral wastes are so deficient in mineral nutrients, that unless some nutrients are added to the developing ecosystem, vegetation will not develop at all, or only very slowly.   However, on some lowland heath soils (e.g. Cannock Chase), the existing mineral nutrient supply may be adequate, and additional nutrients may increase the growth of grasses so that heather establishment is reduced or entirely prevented. In general, nutrient addition appears to be valuable on disturbed deeper peats.

2.6.2 Practical considerations

a)   In general terms, the most successful restoration of heathland has
      been where contractors have paid special attention to the detailed
      requirements of the job, where specifications have been strictly
      adhered to, and where high levels of supervision have been
      maintained.   In-house restoration by conservation organisations
      such as the National Trust or National Parks has often been
      successful because there has been a progressive, well-planned
      programme carried out by well-supervised employees who understand
      the ecological requirements of the restoration process.   Civil
      engineering contractors generally provide poor quality heathland
      restoration.

b)   This view is well supported by the limited record of success in the
      restoration of pipelines.   Many pipeline installations have
      resulted in a failure of heathland restoration or only limited
      success.   The contributary factors have been thoroughly discussed
      in section 2.3.   The key points are that there must be careful
      collection and storage of topsoil, rapid replacement after pipe
      installation with no mixing with subsoil, minimal disturbance to
      non pipe-trench areas, and protection from grazing animals.
      Successful restoration of heathland has been achieved where these
      principles have been adhered to, and where there has been close
      on-site supervision.

c)   Similar arguments apply to restoration of heathland on quarry
      wastes.   Unsuccessful attempts to restore lowland heath in sand and
      gravel quarries in the south of England and East Anglia were mainly
      due to loss of heathland topsoil.   Attempts to apply litter or seed
      capsules to bare mineral substrates failed.   The specific physical
      requirements for germination and establishment of *Calluna*
      and *Erica* spp were not sufficiently appreciated by the quarry
      operators (section 2.1.2).   Key factors contributing to successful
      restoration appear to be : stabilisation of the substrate and
      improvement of microclimate using sown companion grasses, careful
      stripping and adequate replacement of topsoil, a short storage
      period for topsoil, addition of mineral nutrients, and protection
      from trampling and grazing.

d) Larger scale restoration work to cope with the aftermath of
    extensive burns and the effects of extensive erosion is becoming
    more commonplace in the National Parks (e.g. Peak District, North
    York Moors) and elsewhere (e.g. National Trust, Surrey). This type
    of restoration has been designed as a low-cost operation. In
    upland areas, fencing is an expensive item but is essential unless
    management agreements can be reached with tenants, or those with
    rights of common, to substantially reduce livestock densities.

    For heather moorland, a critical factor contributing to successful
    restoration is the creation of a stable substrate by reducing
    surface erosion.   The significance of this is discussed under
    section 2.5.1. and can be achieved by sowing companion grasses or
    by using forestry brashings. Addition of fertiliser, and lime to
    ameliorate the substrate pH encourages the initial establishment of
    the companion grasses. An input of seed or propagules of heathland
    species is usually essential.

    In lowland heath, the same ecological principles apply to the
    restoration process. Grazing may not be a problem, but trampling
    by horses or the general public may be. Thus protection of
    restored areas by fencing may be necessary. Control of erosion
    will be necessary. This may involve filling of deep gulleys with
    subsoil and mechanical grading of badly eroded patches. After
    severe fire in lowland heath, it may be necessary to clear woody
    species before restoration can proceed. Spreading of rotovated
    heathland topsoil, heather litter or seed capsules (on cut shoots)
    will usually be essential for successful restoration. In the long
    term, management of invading woody species and bracken will be
    crucial to the final success of the restoration programme. In
    southern England, the National Trust has achieved this cheaply by
    regular annual or biennial cutting with flail or swipe to maintain
    heather vegetation at a height of 15-20cm without invading shrubs,
    trees or bracken.

e) Generally, rather more intensive and costly techniques have been
    utilised in the restoration of dams, bunds and road embankments,
    (section 2.2.2). Turf-cutting and transplanting programmes must

be well implemented with turves properly handled, transferred and re-positioned. Periods of drought should be avoided if possible, as well as excessive grazing by sheep and rabbits.

Transplanting seedlings or small plants grown from cuttings in paper tubes has been successful in a variety of locations in both upland and lowland heath sites. The work at Robinson's Moss has been very successful (section 2.2.2). Although this approach is labour intensive and thus expensive, it becomes more practical if there is economy of scale when large numbers are produced. Patch planting reduces overall cost per unit area, and where a high cost construction project damages valuable heathland, the expense may be justified. Survival of transplants can be very high (>90%), if properly handled and planted at an appropriate time of year. Spring is satisfactory for upland heath, but not for lowland areas.

Other successful methods of restoration on bunds, dam faces and embankments are similar to those employed in other situations. Use of heather litter, topsoil and macerated vegetation plus topsoil have provided suitable sources of seed and vegetative propagules. Companion grass species have been used successfully, and in some sites addition of mineral nutrients has been beneficial.

f)   A general conclusion from all the work reviewed, both practical and experimental, is that successful restoration of heathland is *technically* feasible in a variety of upland and lowland heaths. However the technology has to be integrated into the overall restoration programme. In a rolling conservation programme this may be easily achieved, but in a civil engineering construction programme, or in a mineral extraction environment, it will be considerably more difficult to achieve practical successful restoration. It can be done if restoration is perceived as an integral and carefully designed part of a whole construction or quarrying programme. The success of this approach has been admirably demonstrated in the sand mining industry in Australia where successful restoration of heath and forest vegetation is routine on a large scale on east and west coasts (Brooks & Bell, 1984; Brooks & Yates, 1980; Clark, 1975).

3.0 METHODS AVAILABLE FOR RESTORATION OF HEATHLAND, AND THEIR APPLICABILITY TO DIFFERENT SITES AND SITUATIONS

The objective of this section is to assess the experimental evidence and the practical experience of using different approaches and different biological resources for restoration, and to provide guidance on choice of methods for restoration or creation of heathland ecosystems. The reasons for restoring heathland at a particular site, the type of site, the practical constraints and the financial input have varied considerably in past work - some methods are not suitable for certain kinds of restoration objective, some methods are more expensive then others but may be justified in particularly sensitive situations.

At any one location, use of combinations of restoration techniques (or resource materials) may be necessary to suit local variations in factors such as landform and visual sensitivity, as well as the physical and chemical nature of the substrate.

Restoration methods are intimately linked with the type of resource material. Thus section 3.0 is structured in terms of heathland resources.

3.1 Turfing - the transfer of blocks of heathland

3.1.1 Evaluation of known examples.

Transfer of heathland turves from a donor to a recipient area undergoing restoration has been done on a large scale only occasionally, but there has also been some small-scale experimental work. A difficulty in attempting to evaluate turfing procedures is that sufficiently accurate records have rarely been made to allow a critical assessment of the methodology.

Turfing has been carried out on a variety of development and mineral extraction sites, and the results are assessed below.

As previously described in section 2.2.2, turves were transplanted at
two dam face sites at Llyn Brenig.   The turves largely failed because
the work was carried out in June 1976 during an unprecedented period of
severe drought.   Also the turves were grazed by sheep, and were
subjected to severe erosion by wind-driven rain during the winter
months.   Where a few of the same turves were carefully placed adjacent
to the Welsh Water Authority offices and were regularly watered,
establishment was successful (Plate 17). Subsequent experimental work by
Meaden (1983) at the same site demonstrated that grazing exclosures and
careful placing of turves in prepared pits gave at least 50% survival
of *Calluna* shoots.

More successful attempts to transfer heathland in blocks have been made
at other sites. For example, upland heath was transplanted directly onto
a coarse china clay waste site (owned by English China Clay
International plc) near St. Stephen, Cornwall (Down pers.comm.1982).
The species composition of the turves was *Calluna vulgaris* 20% (5 to
10 years in age), *Erica cinerea* 5%, *Ulex gallii* 20%, *Festuca
ovina* 40%, and *Molinia caerulea* 10%.   The source site was an area
of moorland near to the waste heap.

The turves were cut by an excavator with a front loading bucket, and
were transplanted in April.   The turves were 0.75m x 2.3m in area and
0.25-0.3m deep.   A total area of 100m² was cut and repositioned, with
the turves tightly packed together.   After three years, survival of all
species was excellent, except that the older plants of *Calluna* had
30 - 50% dead shoots.   However, all the younger *Calluna* plants were
growing satisfactorily.

Transfer of lowland heath has apparently been successfully achieved at
several different locations, and indeed, in Dorset, the cutting of
turves for stabilising surfaces is a traditional practice.

The Suffolk Naturalists Trust undertook the transfer of lowland dry
heath (grass heath) at a superstore construction site in order to
safeguard a breeding colony of the silver-studded blue butterfly. The
transfer took place in midsummer 1985.   A turfing machine removed

heather sections to a depth of 5cm.   The recipient area was bracken-
dominated dry heath on a sandy soil.   The area was sprayed with Asulox
to suppress bracken, then loose surface litter was scraped away, and the
cut turves were placed over the prepared surface.

A verbal report (February 1986) indicated that the turfing operation had
been successful. The timing of turf removal and the shallow depth of
removal should have been unfavourable to a successful outcome.   However,
the cool damp summer weather during 1985 probably assisted the
re-establishment of transferred turves.

Poole Borough Council in Dorset has transferred heather turf on several
occasions.   Lowland heath turves were taken from part of Canford Heath
which was being developed as a housing estate, and were placed at two
recipient sites.   One was at the Poole-Fleets bridge flyover (section
2.2.3) where there was a north west facing embankment with a gradient of
45°.   The turves were laid adjacent to each other directly on subsoil.
Each turf was held in place with chestnut pegs.   The size of turves
was c.45cm x 30cm x 15cm.   They were cut, transported and laid
during February.   Transportation was by tractor and trailer. The area
covered was c. 300m².   Five years after transplanting there was a
dense and relatively even cover of *Calluna* with occasional plants
of *Ulex minor* (dwarf gorse).   On this well-drained site, the species
composition of the vegetation had changed from the original heathland,
which contained *Molinia caerulea* in reasonable abundance, to
heathland with few grasses.   The cost of turfing was estimated at £6 m⁻²
(1979 prices). The only management has been occasional treatment with a
flail (hydraulic, on a long arm) to selectively cut back *Ulex*, which
otherwise would have become too dominant.

The second site was at Rockley Sands, Poole Harbour.   Patches of
heathland were established on an eroding sand cliff embankment (gradient
30°-45°). The turves were laid over bare sand and were held in place
with chestnut pegs and a loose wire mesh.   Each patch was c.3m-4m x
3m-4m in area.

The heathland flora had survived satisfactorily when inspected in May 1984, but some slipping of turves had occurred on the upper slopes and some gaps were present. Overall, the attempt at heathland restoration was reasonably successful, although heathland vegetation was not necessarily an appropriate landscape feature at this site.

Poole Borough Council have also had experience with laying heathland turves on road embankments (Childs, pers.comm.1987). The most successful season for turf transfer has been found to be October/November, although February/March has also been satisfactory. A commercial turf cutting machine has been used in some operations, and although the depth of cut is only 5-7cm, reasonably good establishment has occurred.

Another example relevant to turfing was the very successful restoration of the British Gas Wytch Farm oil pipeline at South Middlebere Heath (Hartland Moor NNR) (section 2.3.3). The temporary removal of heathland and its replacement along the line of the pipe trench was in part a turfing operation, since the excavator removed intact clumps of heather and associated species and these were carefully replaced over the filled pipe trench. In this case the operation occurred during June 1978, and the turves were only in storage for two to three days.

Also in 1978, at Bovington, Dorset, the Public Services Agency (PSA), of the Department of the Environment, placed heathland turves in approximately 3 ha of highly disturbed bare sand and gravel, which had been created by the passage of tanks and various other military vehicles. Turves were cut to a size 30cm x 30cm, and a depth of 15cm, then placed (by hand) in prepared pits and pressed down firmly. The work was carried out in September/October, and all turves were transferred on the day that they were cut and placed singly at three metre centres. There was no treatment of any kind to the adjacent bare substrates. An inspection of the site (Packham, pers. comm. 1986) revealed that after eight years there had been excellent colonisation by heathland plants on the turfed areas, suggesting that restoration using spaced turves can be very successful. However, in this case the treated areas were not assessed regularly, so it is not clear if in the absence of disturbance, the area would have become colonised whether or not the turves were present.

3.1.2   Suggested methods for turfing

Transfer of heather turves is most likely to succeed if the operation is
carried out in early spring or in autumn, when transpiration rates will
be lower than in summer.   Temporary disruption of roots will then be
less important.   Nevertheless, successful transfer of turves during
summer has been achieved (section 3.1.1).

Ideally, heathland containing young plants of *Calluna* and *Erica*
spp (4-10 years in age) should be used for the turf transfer method of
restoration, although often there will be no option but to use heathland
containing much older plants.   Survival of older plants may be enhanced
if the heathland is sprayed with a transpiration inhibitor such as S600
just before turf cutting commences, although this has not been tested.

The depth down the soil profile where turves are cut will be dependent
on the characteristics of the organic horizons and the mineral horizons
below.   On deeper peats, particularly in upland heath, it would be
sensible to remove a turf depth of at least 0.25m and preferably 0.3m -
0.4m.   The less disturbance there is to root and rhizome systems, the
more likely there is to be successful regeneration.   A deep cut may also
be feasible in some lowland wet heath areas.

On lowland dry heath there is often a relatively shallow organic layer,
and below there may be sand or gravel substrates.   Thus it may be
difficult to retain the integrity of turves and this would necessitate a
more shallow depth of cut.

Specialised equipment is not usually available for turf cutting.   A
crawler mounted bucket with a smooth cutting edge has been used
successfully (Lee Moor), as well as a front end loader with toothed
bucket (less ideal) (St.Austell), and various hydraulically operated
excavating equipment.

At Thrislington, near Durham, a specially designed bucket has been used
for cutting deep turves of grassland on a magnesian limestone substrate.

Special equipment would be worth consideration if a major turfing operation is envisaged. Indeed, in relation to the proposed dual oil and gas pipelines (BP and British Gas) from Wytch Farm and Sopley in Hampshire, three areas of heathland will be crossed. A refined turf cutting operation using a specially adapted excavator bucket was tried out in conjunction with Furzebrook Research Staion of the Institute of Terrestrial Ecology. Removal and replacement was very successful, and recovery is being monitored.

If it is necessary to transport turves over some distance, then a trailer will be required, and great care should be taken while loading and unloading the material. Turves will easily break up, and un-necessary handling should be avoided wherever possible.

Depending on the landscaping scheme or the conservation value of the recipient site, turves would normally be placed in tightly packed groups or spaced out over an extensive area. It is not clear whether widely spaced turves would survive successfully if placed on an existing soil/ subsoil surface. In protected lowland heath areas (e.g. Bovington Ranges, Dorset), survival may be good, but in upland sites, erosion and wind exposure would probably cause much damage. Greatly improved survival should be obtained if spaced turves are placed in prepared pits so that the turf is flush with adjacent surrounding soil/subsoil surfaces (Meaden, 1983; Packham, pers. comm. 1986). This applies both to lowland and upland heath. There is a requirement for further research to compare the various turf transplant methods, and to assess the fate of spaced turves.

3.1.3   Advantages and disadvantages of turfing

a)   Advantages

Transfer of turves or large blocks of existing heathland vegetation may be advantageous in some sites. The possible advantages are:

1)   The substrate on which the turves are placed will be stabilised immediately.

2) The complete heathland plant species assemblage should become
    established rapidly, although if environmental conditions are
    changed (e.g. site drainage), some species may disappear or become
    more or less abundant.

3) There will be an immediately favourable visual impact, and the
    reinstated site will blend with surrounding areas of lowland heath
    or heather moorland. Even if irregular patches of turves are
    placed in a background matrix of grasses, the site will probably
    blend more effectively with the surrounding landscape.

4) Normally there will be no requirement for addition of fertiliser,
    and aftercare should be minimal.

5) If a large area is turfed, the adverse effects of grazing animals
    should be reduced. Turves will be less susceptible to grazing
    damage than transplanted seedlings, or seedlings that have become
    established from respread topsoil or litter. There will be a
    substantial cost saving if fencing is not required.

6) If turfing procedures are carried out carefully as recommended
    (section 3.1.2), the probability of achieving a successful
    restoration will be greater than for some other methods, such as
    using heather litter or sowing seed capsules.

b) Disadvantages

The several disadvantages in using transplanted turves are partly
dependent on the characteristics of particular sites and the
availability of appropriate machinery for cutting, transporting and
depositing turves.

1) Turfing is only feasible on a moderate or a large scale where
    industrial development, mineral extraction etc. is already
    destroying an area of heathland or heather moorland. Turves will
    then be available for transportation to the reinstatement site.

2) Other forms of damage to heathlands, such as severe fire or natural
    erosion, will rarely occur at a site where turves can be cut
    without damage to an existing heathland ecosystem.

3) Successful transfer of turves may be restricted to autumn and early
    winter or early spring. The wetness of an area of heather moorland
    or lowland heath will determine whether or not winter operations
    are feasible. There will be a considerable risk of loss of turves
    due to drought if transfer is carried out in late spring or summer.
    This applies particularly to lowland sites and to well-drained
    upland sites such as on a containment bund or the face of a dam.
    Irrigation may be available at some sites, but this will increase
    costs.

4) The most successful transfer of turves probably occurs where there
    is only a short time between cutting and positioning at the
    recipient site. Storage for more than a few days may result in
    desiccation. This may be a restriction on some operations where
    cutting and placing at the recipient site cannot be carefully
    synchronised.

5) The cutting and repositioning of turves may require careful
    supervision of a contractor who does not have previous experience
    of this type of operation. Poor cutting or handling of turves may
    ruin an otherwise carefully planned operation.

6) The age of *Calluna*, *Erica* spp, and other dwarf shrub species
    such as *Vaccinium myrtillus* may be significant in determining
    their ability to survive the shock of being transplanted. Younger
    stands of heather recover more successfully, but at any particular
    site this option may not be available.

7) If appropriate equipment for cutting and transporting turves is not
    readily available at a site, costs will soar. Many quarries and
    industrial development sites will have appropriate equipment
    available. For a long-term or large-scale operation it would be
    advantageous to adapt a bucket specially to increase the efficiency
    of the cutting operation.

8)   Large-scale turfing will only be feasible on relatively gentle
     slopes, although it would be possible to position turves near the
     base of containment bunds or near the top of reservoir dam walls
     where there is appropriate access.

9)   Costs of turfing relative to other methods may be quite high,
     although major determinants of the cost will be the distance over
     which turves are transported and whether or not suitable equipment
     is readily available on site.

3.2   Use of heathland topsoil

3.2.1   Evaluation of past experience

Heathland topsoil has been utilised in reinstatement of upland and
lowland heath in a variety of sites and situations, and there is
sufficient evidence to indicate that this restoration technique is
likely to be successful.

On an experimental scale, topsoil has been removed from the upper
50-100mm of undisturbed heathland soils and replaced either without
further treatment or after breaking up mechanically.   Successful
experiments with heathland topsoil were recorded at Lee Moor, Devon
(2.1.2), and at Robinson's Moss, Derbyshire (2.2.2).   There was also
successful regeneration of the heathland community (Plate 6) at an
English China Clay International plc mica dam site near St.Austell in
Cornwall, where heather moorland topsoil was spread at a depth of about
150mm.

Use of topsoil for heathland reinstatement on a practical rather than
experimental scale has apparently been much less widespread. Mechanical
treatment (e.g. rotovation) has sometimes preceded removal of topsoil
from the donor site.   The approach has usually depended on the
availability of donor heathland which will be destroyed by development
of some kind.

English China Clay International plc has attempted restoration of lowland heath at Blackhill Quarry near Exeter, using topsoil which had been removed with a bucket from a flail mown and rotovated area of adjacent lowland dry heath which was to be destroyed by quarrying operations. At this site, establishment of heath vegetation was partially successful, but could have been more successful had invasion by gorse been prevented.

It has been possible to collect surface horizons (litter plus some topsoil) from areas of heathland where regeneration of the disturbed donor area is an essential landscape amenity requirement. Areas of dry/humid lowland heath at Cannock Chase were flail-mown and then rotovated to a depth of 50mm. The material was collected by hand at this site. Regeneration of the vegetation was relatively rapid, with good cover after three years, and complete recovery of the heathland plant community. The technique was so successful that it was considered to be an appropriate general heathland management method at Cannock Chase.

If the depth of soil organic layers is sufficient that mineral subsoils will not be disturbed, then light surface rotavation of flail-mown areas of heathland may provide a 'once only' source of propagules of native species. This treatment may not be appropriate for older stands of heather (>15 years), where removal of tougher woody plants may cause excessive disturbance to the soil profile.

Another important example of successful topsoil manipulation, in both upland and lowland areas, has been the reinstatement of heathland over pipelines where there was careful preservation and replacement of topsoil. Also the National Trust in Surrey has restored areas of lowland heath which had become invaded by bracken, gorse and trees, often after fire. The areas were cleared of all woody plants and graded with a bulldozer (Plate 18). Although this caused mixing of topsoil and subsoil, at most sites there has been successful regeneration of lowland heath (Plate 19). Further invasion by woody species and bracken has been prevented by regular annual cutting (using a swipe) to a height of 150-200mm.

3.2.2 Suggested methods for the use of topsoil

When an area of heathland is due to be destroyed by quarrying, by construction work or by other sorts of development such as housing, heathland topsoil provides an ideal and relatively cheap source of propagules (i.e. seed and vegetative fragments) of native species. Normally the topsoil source will be relatively close to the recipient site, so that it will contain species which are of an appropriate local genetic race.

The recommended sequence of events in the utilisation of topsoil is as follows:

a)   Dig test pits on the area where topsoil will be removed in order to measure the depth of the organic horizon. If time allows, take samples of the soil profile at 20mm intervals to examine the depth distribution of the seed bank. The method used would be similar to that described for measuring the seed content of heathland litter (Gillham, 1980; section 3.3.2b).   Since a test of the seed and vegetative bud content of topsoil will take at least eight weeks, this can only be carried out where time allows.

b)   Unless the heathland topsoil source area was recently burnt or is covered by young, short vegetation (< 100mm), the area should be flail mown. If there is a deep organic horizon, it should be possible to rotovate the Al, Af and Ao horizons (section 1.6.2.) to a depth of 50-75mm or possibly to 100mm. The soil profile test of seed and vegetative bud content would provide evidence about the optimum depth of rotovation.

c)   Topsoil can be collected for storage and subsequent spreading, using a bucket attached to a tracked vehicle or similar equipment. If there is a shallow organic horizon, particularly on lowland heaths, rotovation is not recommended, as it would mix the seed-bearing topsoil with the lower mineral horizons and greatly dilute the source of propagules. If crawler equipment fitted with a '4 in 1' bucket is used, topsoil should be cleanly stripped to a

recommended depth of 50mm or less, depending on the depth of the
organic horizon.   The topsoil can be broken up in a mechanical
shredder before removal from the site.

d)   Heathland topsoil should be stored in shallow heaps on Terram
     sheet.   In order to prevent excessive compaction, storage heaps
     should not exceed 1.0-1.5m in height.   During winter, storage for
     2-3 months should be possible, without loss of regenerative
     capacity of native species.   In summer, storage time should not
     exceed 2-3 weeks, and preferably should be less.   Seed of *Calluna*
     and *Erica* spp and *Ulex* spp will retain viability for at
     least 14 months in storage heaps (Gillham, 1980), but vegetative
     fragments of species such as *Molinia caerulea*, *Vaccinium
     myrtillus*, *Empetrum nigrum* and *Eriophorum* spp will die
     rapidly in summer conditions.

e)   Heathland topsoil can be spread using manure spreaders, or placed
     in spaced out heaps from a trailer and then level graded with a
     bucket attached to a tracked excavator (drott), or similar type of
     equipment.   A spread depth of 25mm will be adequate for good
     regeneration of heathland species.   Thus it should be possible to
     restore heathland vegetation on an area 1.5 - 2.0 times greater
     than the area from which the topsoil was taken.

f)   When heathland topsoil is spread onto a bare mineral substrate,
     particularly if this has a relatively large particle size (e.g.
     coarse sand or gravel), it is strongly recommended that a mineral
     subsoil of fine particle size is spread over the coarse substrate
     (*c.*100mm in depth).   This will increase the potential mineral
     nutrient reservoir through greater cation exchange capacity, and
     will also provide a potentially larger soil moisture reservoir.

     A heathland vegetation developed more rapidly, with a more
     representative species content, when heathland topsoil was spread
     on a layer of subsoil over coarse sand waste at Lee Moor, Devon,
     than when the subsoil layer was omitted (Putwain & Gillham, 1988).

g)   Usually, grass companion species would be sown on newly-spread
     topsoil (section 3.6), together with an application of fertiliser,

and also crushed limestone when the pH of the topsoil is very low
(e.g. pH 3.5; section 3.7).

On steeper slopes where surface erosion and gulley formation is a
potential problem, topsoil can be stabilised with barley or oats,
and with Geojute netting, which is biodegradable and has a very low
nutrient content.

On fairly level lowland heath areas, reinstatement using topsoil
should be successful if commenced at any time of the year when the
soil is not waterlogged. However, sowing of companion grasses would
be best in early spring, or late summer and early autumn.

In upland heaths, placement of topsoil should be confined to spring
and summer, so that there is adequate time for vegetation to
develop and provide erosion protection in winter.

3.2.3   Advantages and disadvantages in the use of heathland topsoil

a)   Advantages

1)   Topsoil provides an excellent source of seed of *Calluna*
     and *Erica* species, as well as seed, rhizome fragments, rooted
     stem bases and tillers of many other heathland species.

2)   The abundance of plant propagules ensures that a reasonably diverse
     vegetation will become established, and should be representative of
     the local area.

3)   Regeneration of native species from topsoil is usually reasonably
     rapid, and establishment quite successful. Therefore, topsoil is a
     preferred source material for restoration of heathland.

4)   Topsoil is sometimes available as a result of construction or
     quarrying operations, and can be easily stored and utilised at
     appropriate stages in a restoration programme.

5)   Heathland topsoil can be used in a flexible manner to restore
        heathland on large areas of bare substrate, or alternatively,
        to improve or repair smaller areas where previous restoration has
        been poor or where severe fire damage has occurred.

6)   Heathland topsoil is a relatively low-cost source of propagules of
        heathland species. It is easy to collect, handle and respread using
        engineering contractors and farm machinery. Thus large areas can
        be treated at relatively low cost. Normally, it will be possible
        to treat a recipient site which is 1.5 to 2.0 times the surface
        area of the donor site.

7)   Heathland topsoil provides a suitable organic substrate which
        assists establishment of heather seedlings and sown companion
        grasses. On bare mineral substrates, addition of topsoil will
        assist in the retention of applied mineral nutrients.

8)   Topsoil can be used on sites with variable topography, on level
        areas, and on slopes up to 30° provided that stabilisation by
        vegetation occurs soon after spreading.

b)   Disadvantages

1)   Normally heathland topsoil can only be used for restoration if it
        is available because a nearby area of heathland is being destroyed.
        This restricts the kinds of site and situation where topsoil can be
        used. Transport costs will preclude importation from sites more
        than a few miles distant, and the species content of non-local
        sources may be inappropriate to the site where restoration is being
        carried out.

2)   It is only advantageous to use heathland topsoil if it is stored
        for no more than a few weeks before being spread. If stored for
        several months, the vegetative regenerative potential of many
        species will be lost. Seed of some species however will remain
        viable, and heathers, gorse, sedges and rushes are likely to
        dominate in the regenerating plant community.

3)   When heathland topsoil is disturbed, germination of undesirable
     species such as *Betula pendula* or *B.pubescens*, *Ulex* spp
     and *Juncus* spp may be encouraged. Thus continued after-
     management with hand pulling and/or herbicide spot treatments may
     be necessary.   Where an excessive number of rushes become
     established, there is no suitable control treatment.

4)   In some lowland heath sites, the organic topsoil horizon may be
     relatively shallow. The yield of topsoil will be low therefore,
     and there may be contamination by mineral horizons when the topsoil
     is stripped.

3.3   Use of heather litter

3.3.1   Evaluation of past experience

When topsoil or heather turves are unavailable, it will be necessary to
utilise renewable resources of heather propagules and other native
species.

Heather litter was used experimentally on a lowland area at the Oil
Handling Terminal, Flotta, Orkney. Although rates of application to
experimental plots were fairly substantial, the majority of the litter
was lost due to surface erosion. This indicates the vulnerability of
litter if there is not an existing or rapidly established vegetation
cover or other protective material (e.g. forestry brashings) to trap the
litter.

A successful attempt to establish *Calluna* was made on a roadside
embankment near Sheffield (section 2.2.4; Gilbert & Wathern, 1976). In
this situation, rapid establishment of grass cover probably assisted
retention of the litter material. After six years, average *Calluna*
cover was approximately 30%.

Poole Borough Council hydroseeded a road embankment with a mixture of
macerated heathland vegetation (mainly *Calluna*) and litter. The
material was collected from a level area of heath using a combine
harvester. A problem with harvested material is that microbial activity

sometimes causes it to heat up after a few hours. In this instance, the
material was passed over an agricultural drier before storage and
subsequent use.   Three years after the hydroseeding operation,
Calluna and other heathland species were becoming well-established,
although over-all cover is still quite low (Childs, pers.comm.1987).

Heather litter was also effective in small-scale experimental
establishment of *Calluna* at Robinson's Moss, Longdendale, Derbyshire
(section 2.2.2. and Appendix I).   Nine plots (1.5m x 1.5m) on a bare
peat substrate received an application of upland heathland litter. Dry
litter was applied to each plot at a rate equivalent to 2,250kg ha^{-1}.
Fertiliser (17:17:17) was applied at a rate of 200kg ha^{-1}, and ground
limestone was applied at 2,000kg ha^{-1}.

After three years, the mean cover of *Calluna* was 13.3%. The plots
had also been colonised by *Deschampsia flexuosa* which had a mean
cover value of 57.3%.   Although the cover of *Calluna* was only 13.3%,
seedlings were well dispersed throughout the plots, and the *Calluna*
content of the vegetation was progressively increasing.

Calluna and *Erica* spp were successfully established by English
China Clay International plc on a small area (0.5ha) of mineral sand
waste near St.Austell in Cornwall. Heather litter was spread by hand
over the area. The rate of spread was not recorded. After four years,
there was a modest cover of heathers. On another area of mineral waste
near Plympton in Devon, locally collected lowland heathland litter was
applied to 1.0m x 1.5m plots on two types of substrate, fine tailings
and coarse killas waste rock. The rate of application was 2,000kg ha^{-1}
of litter, and all plots were sown with a mixture of *Agrostis
castellana* and *A. vinealis* as companion species. After three
years, the plots on the fine tailings had become dominated by gorse
(*Ulex europaeus*), since seed of this species had been a component of
the litter. On the killas substrate there was successful regeneration
of *Calluna*, *Erica cinerea*, *Molinia caerulea* and *Agrostis curtisii*,
without excessive numbers of gorse plants. The killas site was on a
well-drained slope susceptible to drought, which may have reduced
germination of gorse. Compared to areas where heathland topsoil had
been spread, the rate of development of vegetation cover was

considerably less. This was probably because there was also vegetative regeneration of many species in the topsoil, whereas regeneration was entirely from seed in the litter.

At Cannock Chase Country Park, experiments were carried out to restore heather cover on an old quarry site with a bare gravel substrate (Daniels, pers.comm. 1983). Plots were laid out with rabbit-proof and deer-proof fencing. Soil was shallowly or deeply rotovated and certain plots received NPK fertiliser (15:15:15) at a rate of 100kg ha^{-1}. *Deschampsia flexuosa* was sown at a rate of 58kg ha^{-1}. Fresh litter was broadcast by hand at a rate of 500cm^3 m^{-2} (equivalent to approximately 70g of dry litter m^{-2}, and considerably less than amounts used at other sites). In 1983, after four years, heather cover was very low (1.7-2.5%) and the area was dominated by grasses and gorse.

The conclusion is that use of heather litter has not always been a successful approach to reinstatement of *Calluna*, *Erica* spp and other native heathland plants, particularly on bare surfaces where it may blow away or suffer surface erosion.

3.3.2   Recommendations for the use of heather litter

a)   Collection of litter

Litter may be collected from most areas of upland or lowland heath without causing unacceptable damage or disturbance, except possibly temporary disruption to some animal species. Collection by hand has been the main method utilised in the past. Experience of litter collection by the EAU indicates that 30-40 kg of dry litter can be obtained per man-day at an upland site in the Clwydian Hills where litter is abundant. This was sufficient to spread over 250-300m^2 at an application rate of 125g m^{-2}.

At Cannock Chase, 550-600 litres of litter were collected per man-day, and this was spread over 1,100-1,200m^2 (i.e. approximately 700 kg ha^{-1} (70g m^{-2})). It is difficult to equate volume and rate, but this application rate was substantially less than that of the EAU.

In upland heaths, medium-aged stands (10-15 years) of heather appear optimum for collection of litter by hand. Considerable quantities will have accumulated and are easily collected. Old heather contains an excessive number of partly buried prostrate stems, which interfere with collection. On many lowland heath sites, accumulation of litter is much less, and the collection rate will be considerably less than the rates quoted above. In Dorset heaths, the older stands of vegetation (15-25 years) may provide the most abundant litter.

Litter has also been collected by 'Billy Goat' vacuum litter collectors, which perform reasonably efficiently on areas of dry heath where the vegetation is short or has been recently burnt. In this situation, previous raking of the area to loosen the surface increases the quantity of litter collected, which can amount to 80-100kg of dry litter per machine per day. A large machine providing a powerful vacuum and an extension tube will assist effective litter collection.

In some areas it may be possible to flail older heather, rake off the mangled vegetation, lightly rotovate the top 5 cm, and then collect the litter using a 'Billy Goat'. Since flail treatment of heathland vegetation can be a useful management technique to encourage regeneration of *Calluna*, litter collection could be concentrated on areas which would benefit from a flail treatment. This approach proved successful at Cannock Chase, although litter was subsequently collected by hand.

An interesting development resulted from collection of heather litter on Flotta, Shetland. Heathland areas which were vacuumed in March 1976, using a Billy Goat litter collector, produced a substantially greater number of *Calluna* seedlings per unit area during spring and summer of the same year. Vacuumed areas had a mean number of seedlings per m^2 of 37.8, whereas undisturbed areas had a *Calluna* seedling density of 13.4. per m^2. Removal of loose litter is known to encourage germination of *Calluna*.

b) Assessment of heather litter for seed content

It is advisable to check the germinable seed content of litter to ensure
that the material has a good regeneration potential. Weighed amounts of
sieved litter should be spread thinly (2mm) on a layer (25-40mm) of an
acid peat/sand mixture or on an unlimed sterilised compost placed in
seed trays. The trays should be put into a glasshouse mist spray unit
maintained at 18°-25°C.

Emergence of ericoid seedlings (*Calluna* and *Erica* spp) should be
recorded for a period of twelve weeks which will encompass the majority
(>90%) of germinable seeds. Thus the potential number of seedlings per
unit weight of litter can be assessed. This will not correspond to the
total ericoid seed content of the litter, since some seeds will remain
viable but dormant.

Most heather litter will contain germinable seed of various native
non-ericoid species. Particularly common is seed of *Ulex* spp,
Betula spp, *Molinia caerulea* and *Juncus* spp. Some of these
species will be undesirable components of a regenerating heathland
vegetation.

The rate of application of litter should be sufficient to provide a
minimum of 300-500 germinable seeds per m². The majority of litters
tested by EAU would provide the necessary seed numbers if spread at the
recommended application rate of 1,000-1,500kg ha⁻¹.

c) Storage of litter

Once collected, heather litter should be spread out in a suitable area,
thoroughly dried and then put through a coarse sieve to remove residual
vegetation fragments, dead stems etc. Once dry, the litter can be
stored for at least three to four years in paper or fibre sacks in a
cold store, or in a dry storage area. EAU experience indicates that
seed of *Calluna* and *Erica* spp remains viable in the stored
litter. Freshly collected damp litter could be stored outside during
the winter in fibre bags or in any appropriate container; this would be
unwise during warmer spring and summer periods, when fermentation and
consequent heating may kill propagules.

d)   Spreading of litter

There are few reports of appropriate techniques for spreading heather
litter.   On a small scale (< 0.5ha), scattering by hand should be
satisfactory technically, and cost-effective.   For larger areas, it may
be feasible to spread litter using a tractor-mounted fertiliser spreader
or a mulch blower.

Application of litter by hydroseeding was used on embankments at
Povington Heath, Lulworth, Dorset, during Spring 1986.   At this newly
constructed tank target site, heathland litter was a component of a
grass seed/mulch/fertiliser mixture, appropriate for reinstatement of
lowland dry heath.   As yet (autumn 1987), there are no available records
of the success or otherwise of the operation.

In experiments reviewed under section 3.3.1, application rates have been
mainly in the range 1,000-2,000kg ha^{-1}.   At some sites, this has
resulted in adequate heather seedling densities.   In lowland heath
areas, 1,250-1,500 kg ha^{-1} should be adequate, although higher rates may
be required in upland sites to compensate for potential losses by wind
and erosion.

The cost of hand collection, storage and hand spreading of heather
litter is estimated to be £2,000 - £2,500 ha^{-1}.   This is based on a
requirement (sufficient for 1ha) of forty man-days for collection (at
£40 per day), eight man-days for spreading, plus storage and transport
costs.   If farm implements are used to collect and spread litter, the
estimated cost is £1,200 - £1,500 ha^{-1}, where the cost of hire of
tractor, machinery and driver is £150 per day.

3.3.3 Advantages and disadvantages of using heather litter.

a)   Advantages

1.   Heathland litter provides a suitable source of propagules of
      Calluna and *Erica* spp for reinstatement of small areas
      (<0.5ha) if hand labour is employed, or for larger areas if the
      collection and spreading operations are mechanised.

2)   Litter can be used to repair small areas where an initial
        heathland reinstatement has been patchy in its regeneration, or
        where existing low density and moribund grass swards on low
        fertility soils could be improved by conversion to heathland.
        Colonisation by heathers would initiate the conversion process.

3)   Litter is relatively easy to handle, and can be stored dry for
        periods of several years without loss of seed viability.

4)   Litter is easy to spread by hand and would probably spread easily
        using farm machinery. Litter could be included in seed mixtures
        for hydroseeding.

b)   Disadvantages

1)   It will not always be possible to find suitable heathland areas
        for litter collection, particularly in lowland heaths. However,
        in heathland vegetation where litter is abundant, it is easy to
        collect by hand, and also efficient collection should be possible
        using a 'Billy Goat' combined with the use of a flail and
        tractor-mounted rotovator.

2)   Litter will usually contain germinable seed of only a limited
        number of native species. Topsoil or turves will provide for the
        regeneration of a more species-rich plant community. When litter
        is used, species other than *Calluna* and *Erica* spp will
        only gradually colonise a reinstated area by immigration.

3)   Litter may contain excessive numbers of seed of undesirable
        species such as *Betula* spp or *Ulex europaeus*. This partly
        depends on the location where it is collected. Thus provision may
        have to be made for subsequent herbicide treatments, hand-pulling
        or cutting treatments to control undesirable species.

4)   The rate of application of litter should be sufficient normally to
        provide at least 300-500 germinable heather seeds m^2, so ideally,
        litter should be tested for heather seed content before it is
        used. This would create a delay of at least 10 - 12 weeks.

5)   On an experimental scale, use of litter has not always been
      successful in introducing heathers to a restored area. To prevent
      loss by wind and surface erosion, litter should be introduced with
      a rapidly establishing short-lived companion grass, plus slower-
      growing native grasses.

3.4 Use of commercial seed and harvested heather shoots

3.4.1 Evaluation of performance on different sites.

A considerable number of attempts at restoration of heathland have been
made using harvested heather shoots which bear mature seed capsules, or
using commercial supplies of heather seed capsules.   Many of the
attempts at large-scale restoration have been carried out relatively
recently, so that there is inadequate evidence concerning the success of
the technique over a period of several years.   Most of the restoration
work has been on upland heath areas.   The quantities of seed, capsules
or cut material applied are summarised in Table 3.1.

Major restoration work using cut heather shoots is being carried out in
the North York Moors National Park at Glaisdale Moor. Areas of bare peat
were limed, fertilised and seeded with *Deschampsia flexuosa* and
Agrostis capillaris as nurse/companion grasses.   Cut heather was
applied later, to the established sward (section 2.5.2).   After three
growing seasons good results were reported. By summer 1986, establishment of both species of grasses had been generally successful, and
heather seedlings had begun to appear in moderate numbers.

The majority of the evidence for successful establishment of *Calluna*
from cut shoots involves relatively small-scale experimental work. At
Robinson's Moss (2.2.3. and App. I[2.1]), one of the treatments involved
sowing seed capsules (commercially obtained and of Dutch origin) at a
rate of 45 kg ha^{-1}.   The seed capsules were sown with companion grass
species, fertiliser and ground limestone.

Results after five years indicated that a very small population of
Calluna had established, usually only 1 to 3 plants m^{-2} with cover
values of <5%.   There was no measurement of the original viability of
the seed.   Since the *Calluna* seed capsules and the grass seed were

Plate 9. Robinson's Moss : an aerial view of large-scale and
small-plot experiments. The large-scale experiment on
the left of the fenced area has been established five
months and is not open to grazing by sheep.

Plate 10. Robinson's Moss : a part of the large-scale heathland
restoration experiment, located on an originally bare
sloping peat surface. After two years, there is
excellent establishment and growth of *Calluna* and
Deschampsia in fenced areas.

Plate 11. Robinson's Moss : profusely flowering *Calluna vulgaris*
          established from cuttings grown in paper tubes, two years
          after transplanting within the large-scale experiment.

Plate 12. A 24 inch (610mm) gas pipeline, seven years after being
          laid, at Ilkley Moor in Yorkshire, showing colonisation
          by rushes in wetter areas.

Plate 13. A 36 inch (910mm) gas pipeline, three years six months after installation, at the Whitfield estate, Northumberland, showing minimal colonisation by native moorland species.

Plate 14. A 10 inch (255mm) gas pipeline, six years after installation across the Pentland Hills near Edinburgh. Note the grassy areas on the original pipetrench and subsoil storage zones, but good *Calluna* regeneration elsewhere.

Plate 15. An 8 inch (205mm) oil pipeline laid in 1976 across
Hartland Moor NNR in Dorset. Note that two years four
months after installation, the regeneration of *Calluna*,
Erica spp and other native heath species is excellent.

Plate 16. Heathland regeneration on a severely burnt area at
Moel Famau Country Park, Clwydian Hills. Protection from
grazing by sheep was the only requirement for successful
restoration of *Calluna*.

Table 3.1   **Quantities of heather seed, capsules or cut shoots**
                   applied in heathland restoration experiments

Site and experiment	Quantity of seeds, capsules or cut shoots applied	Results
Peak District National Park, Moorland restoration experiments (Tallis & Yalden, 1983)	312g cut shoots m^{-2}	Variable depending on site and experimental treatment: 16 seedlings m^{-2} up to >300m^{-2} after 18 months.
Peak District National Park, Robinson's Moss, (EAU, Liverpool University.)	45kg ha^{-1} commercial seed capsules. Dutch origin.	Very poor. 1 to 3 plants m^{-2} after 5 years.
Peak District National Park, Holme Moss (Anderson, pers.comm.1987)	0.3ha of *Calluna* cut and spread onto 0.6 ha of bare ground.	Very good. Percentage cover of *Calluna* was 11.4% after 3 years.
Cavenham Heath, Norfolk (Lowday, 1984)	20,000 seeds m^{-2} of *Calluna*	Excellent. After 5 years cover of *Calluna* was 10.1 to 68.4%
Cannock Chase Country Park (Daniels, pers.comm. 1983)	5kg ha^{-1} locally collected seed capsules.	Poor. A few seedlings. No quantitative data.
British Gas pipeline Haltwhistle, Durham, (Meaden, 1983)	225g cut shoots m^{-2}	2-3 seedlings m^{-2}, up to 15 m^{-2} after 7 months
North Yorks Moors National Park, (Auld, pers.comm. 1986, Brown, pers.comm. 1986)	12g "seed" m^{-2} (1979/80) 1000kg ha^{-1} seed (1985)	Delay in germination of 18 to 24 months due to unfavourable climatic conditions

sown simultaneously, it is probable that many of the capsules were blown away before the grasses emerged and effectively trapped the capsules. It is better to broadcast capsules into an established sward of low plant density.   When entire cut heather shoots are spread, loss of capsules would be much less of a problem, since they mostly remain attached to the shoots for a few weeks. It is also possible that the Dutch lowland heath strain of *Calluna* suffered high seedling mortality in the extreme environment at Robinson's Moss.

A series of experiments which provide excellent evidence of the effectiveness of heather seed input as cut heather-bearing seed capsules, are those established by the Moorland Restoration Project team in the Peak District National Park (section 2.4.2). In treatments where there was heather seed input, 5 kg of cut heather shoots (wet weight) were applied to the 4m x 4m plots in February or March. The heather was cut in December using an Allen scythe, and collected by hand. After 18 months, seedling numbers were very variable dependent upon site and protection from grazing. In fenced plots (except Holme Moss "N.E. mineral"; Table 2.2), average *Calluna* seedling numbers varied from *c.* 16 m^{-2} at Burbage Moor, to *c.*70 m^{-2} at Holme Moss S.W. and to 300 m^{-2} at Holme Moss "N.E. peat".   At Burbage Moor after three years, cover of *Calluna* had reached 40%.

A short experiment carried out by Liverpool University on a British Gas pipeline route (at the Whitfield Estate in Northumberland) involved the spreading of cut heather-bearing seed capsules in October at a rate of 2,250 kg ha^{-1} fresh weight of shoots. After only seven months, the number of *Calluna* seedlings per unit area varied from 2-3 m^{-2} up to 15 m^{-2}.

The experimental work carried out by Lowday (1984) at Cavenham Heath, Suffolk (2.4.2) also showed that input of *Calluna* seeds was crucial for the re-establishment of lowland heath in areas where bracken had been killed by spraying with asulam.

In none of the experiments quoted above were the seed capsules deliberately exposed to high temperatures before they were sown. However, it is known (Whittaker & Gimingham, 1962) that seed germination is stimulated by heat treatment (e.g. moorland burning) such as 20 to 30 seconds at 120-160°C or several hours at 70-80°C. If harvested cut heather shoots are artifically dried (in an agricultural drier) before spreading, this may stimulate germination.

3.4.2   Methods of harvesting and spreading seed capsules

Cutting should be carried out in October-December when capsules are mature, but before too much seed has been dispersed.   Since capsules remain attached to plants for many weeks, the window of operation is flexible.

In lowland heaths, it should be possible to take a forage harvester across areas where cutting is a required form of management (Plate 20). Often this will involve harvesting from existing fire breaks where young heather has grown sufficiently and where there is profuse flowering. This should maximise the proportion of seed capsules to leaf and stem. The height of cut should be adjusted to the height of the heather, so that not too much woody biomass is collected.   Poole Borough Council has successfully used a combine harvester to collect shoots and seed capsules.   In upland areas, forage harvesters and balers have also been used successfully, where terrain is suitable for their use.

An alternative approach which could be used in December when temperatures are lower, would be to cut with a flail mower and collect with a baler. The bales could be stored outdoors until early spring.

Transportation costs and the type of agricultural equipment used will preclude carting heather over distances in excess of a few kilometres (unless baled heather is transported). Thus it will be feasible only to utilise local heathland areas, which is an advantage from the point of view of conserving local plant populations.

Once cut, it is best to spread heather shoots bearing seed capsules within hours, since a large heap of material will tend to heat up. The cut material should be carted in trailers for spreading either by hand, flinging the heather shoots over the back of a trailer, or using an agricultural muck spreader.   Some trailer attachments for forage

harvesters allow the cut material to be unloaded from the back, thus
making it possible to harvest, transport and spread with one set of
equipment.

If a restoration programme is unable to cater for spreading immediately
after cutting, then cut heather could be dried over an agricultural
drier and baled subsequently. Alternatively, in late autumn with the
onset of cold weather, heather shoots could be cut and baled directly,
particularly at high altitudes.

Cut shoots can be spread during autumn or early spring (February-March).
Spring-spread heather capsules may produce a flush of seedlings in the
autumn, or sometimes not until the autumn of the following year.
Capsules may not break up and decompose in dry summer conditions, and in
any event, lack of moisture will inhibit germination and establishment
of ericoid seedlings. If few heather seedlings emerge during the first
year, failure must not be assumed until a second or even a third growing
season has passed by.

The rate of spread of cut heather shoots has not been clearly defined,
since capsule number per unit weight of shoots will vary with the age of
plants, height of cut etc. More critical research is required to
establish the yield of capsules from different types of harvesting and
from different ages of heather etc.

There is conflicting and inadequate evidence concerning the amount of
heather seed which should be applied per unit area. Available
information is summarised in Table 3.1. It is difficult to make any
accurate quantitative comparison between heather supplied as cleaned
seed, as dried seed capsules or as cut heather shoots.

Overall, there is little sense in applying cleaned seed, and there is
insufficient data to recommend a spreading rate for dry capsules. A
tentative recommendation is that a wet weight of between 400g and 600g
m^{-2} of freshly cut heather shoots bearing an abundance of mature seed
capsules should be applied to obtain a satisfactory population density
of *Calluna* and *Erica* seedlings.

3.4.3   Advantages and disadvantages of using cut heather shoots

a)   Advantages

1)   Suitable areas of heathland for harvesting heather will often be located near to where heathland restoration is proceeding.   In lowland heaths, fire breaks may provide the most suitable locations for cutting.

2)   Cut heather shoots are a renewable resource, and collection can be planned to cause minimum possible disturbance to the donor heath-land habitat.   Therefore substantial supplies can be harvested, which will enable large areas to be treated.   Turves, topsoil or litter will rarely be available in sufficient quantities for large scale heathland restoration.

3)   Harvested heather is a cheap source of propagules. If the operation can be mechanised using agricultural machinery, then unit costs should be relatively low. A conservative estimate indicates that two men plus equipment could harvest at least 2ha per day, and that 4,000kg of harvested material should be adequate to restore 4ha. Costs for collection and spreading could be as low as £150 ha^{-1}.

4)   Cut heather shoots can be spread over recently established companion grass swards or on older grassland, provided that grass tiller density is low and there are many suitable gaps for *Calluna* or *Erica* seedling establishment.   Alternatively, cut heather can be spread on bare substrates, and forestry brashings spread to protect microsites for heather germination and establishment.   The cut heather stems themselves will provide protection for seedlings of *Calluna* if the rate of spread is sufficient, so forestry brashings may not be essential.   Clearly there is flexibility in the use of cut heather during a heathland restoration programme.

5)   Introducing *Calluna* or *Erica* spp by seed is suitable for
     lowland heaths only where supplies of litter or topsoil may be
     scarce or non-existent. Cut heather shoots are often the only
     resource for the majority of lowland heath restorations.

b)   <u>Disadvantages</u>

1)   Cut heather shoots will usually only introduce *Calluna* and
     Erica species. Seed of other native species will have
     dispersed before the heather shoots are cut. Thus spreading cut
     heather is only a partial answer to full restoration of heathland
     vegetation.

2)   Collection of cut heather shoots is limited to October and
     November. Wet weather in autumn may limit access by machinery to
     some sites and further restrict the 'collection window'. A missed
     opportunity in a particular year will enforce a ten month delay in
     collecting seed-bearing material.

3)   Problems of storage of cut heather are greater than for litter or
     topsoil. The material is bulky but can be baled. In cool upland
     locations, bales could be stacked outdoors. Dried cut heather could
     be stored under cover in bulk. If cut heather is to be utilised
     effectively, good forward planning is essential.

3.5 <u>Transplants : cuttings or seedlings grown in paper tubes or
     multipots; bare-root nursery stock</u>

3.5.1   Experimental and practical experience

There have been a few attempts at transplanting heathers either as
bare-rooted plants or grown in paper tubes, fibre minipots, or nursery
containers.

An experimental approach to restoration of heathland using plants raised
from cuttings and grown-on in biodegradable paper tubes has been
developed and tested by the EAU, in both upland and lowland heath
sites.

Cuttings were taken from indigenous populations of *Calluna* (and *Erica tetralix* on one occasion), and were grown-on and eventually transplanted back into areas of heath restoration. Survival was excellent, and the transplants grew rapidly in both upland and lowland sites. Excellent heather cover has been achieved after just three growing seasons, and the method clearly has potential for application in practical restoration work.

In May 1983, at Robinson's Moss (section 2.2.2), *Calluna* transplants grown in paper tubes were placed in deep peat substrates and also in shallow peat over millstone grit. Immediately before planting the area was treated with crushed limestone (2,500kg ha^{-1}), and fertiliser as ICI No.5 (200kg ha^{-1}) and as Superphosphate (100kg ha^{-1}). Patches of *Calluna* (approximately 1.0m – 1.5m x 0.75m – 1.25m) were created in a background matrix of sown companion grasses (*Deschampsia flexuosa* and *Agrostis castellana*). Transplant density was 25-30 plants m^{-2}, but this proved to be too dense. Therefore 10 plants m^{-2} were removed later after 28 months.

Two growing seasons after planting there was profuse flowering, and after three growing seasons, percentage cover of *Calluna* was >80% on the deep peat areas but only 25-30% on the shallow peat over millstone grit. Mean plant height ranged from 16.9 to 26.8cm (on deep peat), and mean plant diameter was 19.8cm – 31.2 cm.

By the end of the third growing season (September 1985), seedlings of *Calluna* had established on the periphery of the patches of transplanted *Calluna*. Few seedlings were more than 40cm distant from the edge of a patch. Nevertheless this was a most encouraging indication that *Calluna* will eventually colonise the areas of stable grass vegetation.

Field trials were established at Pyestock Wood (RAE, Farnborough, Hampshire) in an attempt to restore heather vegetation on acid sand substrates (pH 4.1-4.5) derived from Bagshot Beds. Treatments comprised addition of limestone at 2,000kg ha^{-1}, fertiliser (ICI No.5) at rates of 150 and 300kg ha^{-1}, plus Enmag at 150kg ha^{-1}. The following grass seed mixture was sown at a rate of 100kg ha^{-1}:

40%   *Agrostis castellana* cv. Highland
35%   *Festuca rubra* ssp pruinosa cv. Merlin.   .
10%   *Festuca rubra* ssp. commutata cv. Waldorf
 5%   *Festuca longifolia* cv. Scaldis
10%   *Deschampsia flexuosa*

Heather plants which had been pre-grown in paper tubes were planted at a density of 4 m^{-2}.   Diameter of individuals at planting was 7-13cm. After 2½ years, growth was good on most of the treatment combinations, including the untreated control, with a mean plant diameter of 16-18 cm and a mean height of 17-18 cm.

It is also feasible to raise *Calluna* or *Erica* from seed, using litter collected from areas of heather moorland or lowland heath. The advantage is that seedlings can be raised at any time of the year, whereas taking of cuttings is restricted to late spring, summer and early autumn.

The success of the technique was tested at Marchlyn Mawr, near Llanberis, Gwynedd, where the CEGB operate a pumped storage power station (2.2.2). Calluna seedlings were raised in plastic multipots in a heated glasshouse at the Bangor University field station, then transplanted without the pots into the face of the dam at the upper reservoir. A minor drawback of using litter as a seed source was that multiple germination occurred and there were several seedlings per pot. If too many seedlings emerge, some thinning may be necessary.

There is little experience of the direct use of heather transplants. At the Birchwood Brook Linear Park in Warrington, Cheshire, 250 *Calluna* plants (1-2 years old) were transplanted during April from a nearby moss into a peaty soil.   The plants were placed at 30-35cm intervals. Survival after two years was excellent, with only 10% mortality.

Near the previous site, 2,000 bare rooted native *Calluna* plants (3-4 years old) which had been grown in a nursery in Dorset were planted in December into a clay soil mixed liberally with peat.   There was 50-60% survival, with frost-heaving apparently contributing to mortality.

Cuttings of *Vaccinium myrtillus* and *Empetrum nigrum* can also be raised in small containers. These species, along with *Calluna*, were transplanted in order to restore heathland vegetation around car parks in the vicinity of Anson's Bank, Cannock Chase (Countryside Commission, 1985a).

3.5.2 Methods for producing and planting out seedlings and rooted cuttings

a) Raised seedlings

The following procedures for raising heather seedlings in substantial numbers are based on work carried out by Ellis at Pen-y-Ffridd (Bangor University), and by the Environmental Advisory Unit (Liverpool University).

1) Collect heather litter from the site which is to be restored (or from a suitable local area).

2) Screen litter to remove any stones, twigs, etc.

3) Mix litter with John Innes No.1 potting compost (without added lime) in a 1:1 ratio and spread this in a thin layer on compost in plastic multipots, fibre jiffy pots, or paper tubes.

4) A suitable compost for multipots or tubes comprises 50% John Innes No.1 potting compost (without lime) and 50% coarse sand (0.5mm-2.0mm). It will probably be worthwhile to add to the compost a modest amount of a slow-release fertiliser such as Osmocote (3-4 month formulation).

5) Keep multipots, jiffy pots or paper tubes in a glasshouse, (unheated in spring and summer, or heated in winter), and keep the litter continually moist using a mist spray unit or spray line.

6)   Many seedlings of *Calluna* and/or *Erica* species will appear
     within 3-4 weeks, and during spring or summer it should be
     possible to transfer seedlings outdoors after 6-8 weeks. At this
     time a liquid feed of NPK fertiliser (in equal proportions) should
     enhance seedling growth if Osmocote was not added to the compost
     initially. Seedlings should have reached a size appropriate for
     planting out in the field after 17-20 weeks.

b)   Rooted cuttings

The procedures for raising rooted cuttings are based on long experience
of horticultural growers who raise plants of garden cultivars, and also
on the experience of the EAU over five years of rooting cuttings from
wild plants of *Calluna*.

1)   Cuttings should be collected from wild plants at or near the site
     of heathland restoration, or from a nursery collection of stock
     plants which were originally collected from the restoration site.

2)   Young, vigorously growing shoots (length 3-4cm) can be taken in
     spring, summer or autumn until October. Where a stock collection
     is available, it is usual for several hundred cuttings to be
     collected from each well-grown plant.

3)   *Calluna vulgaris*, *Erica tetralix* and *E.ciliaris* are
     relatively easy to root. *Calluna* will root successfully in
     spring, summer and autumn, but the other species will probably
     root most successfully in summer only. It is more difficult to
     obtain successful rooting in cuttings of *E. cinerea* and *E.
     vagans* (Fyfe-Maxwell & Patrick, 1966; van de Laar, 1978).

4)   Cuttings should be rooted in a cold frame, or under a mist
     propagation unit in a heated greenhouse, or in a frame with
     electrical soil heating. Bottom heat is an advantage since
     cuttings root more rapidly. Cuttings rooted in mist with bottom
     heat should be ready for transplanting in 3-4 weeks.

5)   A suitable compost for cuttings is two or three parts peat to one part sharp sand, with addition of some heathland soil to provide necessary mycorrhizae. Dipping each cutting in hormone powder (e.g. Seradix) prior to planting will normally aid rooting.

6)   When cuttings have become well-rooted, they should be transplanted into paper tubes using a compost similar to that used for seedlings (3.5.2a). Cuttings rooted in spring or early summer will be ready to transplant into the field 12-15 weeks after they were planted into paper tubes. Late summer and autumn cuttings should be held over until spring for planting out.

7)   It is possible to apply a similar approach to raising plants of *Empetrum nigrum* and *Vaccinium myrtillus*. However, this latter species is much more difficult to root succesfully, and only a few rooted cuttings may be obtained.

c)   <u>Planting out in the field</u>

1)   Before planting out in the field, the rooted cuttings or seedlings should be thoroughly soaked by standing in a tray of water. On planting out, it is important that damage to the root system is minimised.

2)   In many exposed situations, particularly on slopes, it will be advisable to plant heather seedlings into an already established low density sward (or recently sown area) consisting of appropriate companion grass species. This should prevent erosion occurring around the base of the transplanted seedlings, and will help to stabilise the substrate.

3)   In order to provide a reasonable stand of heather within 4-5 years, it is suggested that the minimum planting density for seedlings and cuttings should be around 10-15 per m^2. The young transplants should be arranged in irregularly shaped patches to provide an appropriate landscape character. The size of a patch would depend on the particular characteristics of the site being restored, but should probably be at least 50-100m^2 to be effective visually.

4)   The optimum timing of planting out in the field will depend on the
      elevation and geographical location of the site. In southern
      lowland situations, planting in September/October and February/
      March would probably be best to ensure successful establishment.
      In upland and northern locations, the planting season could be
      extended to February/May and late August/October.

5)   Protection from grazing animals will be essential for 3-5 years,
      depending on local grazing management and stocking rates.

6)   It would normally be much too expensive to cover an entire
      restoration area with heather plants. Thus irregularly-shaped
      patches of heather planted in a background grass matrix will
      provide foci for subsequent spread of heather by seed
      dissemination.

3.5.3   Advantages and disadvantages of using heather transplants

a)   Advantages

1)   A good cover of heather and an attractive landscape will be
      attained more rapidly from transplants than from sown seed,
      heather litter or topsoil. The time taken to create a
      satisfactory heather cover will depend partly on the density of
      planting, but could be as little as three growing seasons.

2)   Transplanting heather seedlings directly from natural habitats may
      be advantageous where there is a nearby area of heathland which
      has been carefully burnt 2-4 years previously. It is possible to
      collect 1-2 year old seedlings using a bulb planter to extract
      them without causing unacceptable damage to the area. A sufficient
      number of seedlings must be left to allow continued heather
      regeneration in the burnt area.

3)   If collection of seedlings in the field is impossible, heather
      seedlings are easily raised from litter which can be collected
      from heathland near or at the site which is being reinstated.
      Large numbers of seedlings can be raised in small containers such
      as paper tubes, fibre minipots or small plastic multipots, and can

be transplanted after one season's growth with minimal root disturbance.   Most good quality plant nurseries could raise seedlings on contract at relatively low cost.

4)   Cuttings develop into suitably sized plants for transplanting into a restored site more rapidly than seedlings. Cuttings provide the potential for introducing a wider range of heathland species than the use of litter or harvested seed.

b)   Disadvantages

1)   A minimum density of about 15 plants m^{-2} would be required to provide a satisfactory heather cover within two growing seasons. This assumes that mortality of transplants would be relatively low (<20%). The planting would have to be done in patches only, since to plant 100,000-150,000 plants ha^{-1} to attain complete cover would be prohibitively expensive at £15,000 per ha at least for plants alone.   Planting costs of at least £7,000 per ha would be extra.

2)   Transplanting heather seedlings or cuttings is not really feasible on a very large scale. The optimum approach would be to establish patches of transplants. If 10% of the total restored area were to be planted with *Calluna* or *Erica* spp the total cost of plants and planting would be only about £5,000 ha^{-1}. Such a cost would be justified in areas of special landscape amenity value.

3)   Older container-grown nursery stock (or bare-rooted transplants) of native *Calluna* or *Erica* spp is not only difficult to find, but is also very expensive, and available only in small quantities.

4)   Protection from grazing (by sheep, and possibly by rabbits) would be essential for the young heather transplants, and would further inflate the costs.

3.6   Companion grass species and cultivars

The primary role of companion or nurse species is to stabilise bare and/

or eroding substrates so that seedlings of *Calluna* and *Erica* spp and other native heathland species can become established. Seedlings of heathers are very small and are particularly prone to disturbance, even on a microtopographical scale.

However, there is a delicate balance between having species which will establish and grow rapidly to stabilise a bare substrate and having species which are not excessively competitive. Seedlings of heathers are very susceptible to competition. Other native heathland species, even if they regenerate from rhizomes or buds on rootstocks etc. are also susceptible to competition. Thus companion species may have to be sown in mixtures to provide the necessary properties.

The secondary role of companion species is to provide a suitable micro-environment at the soil surface which will encourage germination and establishment of heathland plants.

3.6.1   Experience in using companion grasses

Small scale experimental work has shown which species and commercial cultivars make useful companion (or nurse) species for stabilising bare substrates and thus aiding the development of native heath vegetation. Large scale restoration projects with mixtures of species provide less useful results, as it is rarely possible to determine which of the sown species is providing the stability and which the companion species role.

Gillham's experiments at an upland site at Lee Moor (App.I [1.1]) demonstrated that *Agrostis castellana* (sown at a rate of 15kg ha⁻¹) provided good surface stabilisation and was an excellent companion species.   In the same experiment, *Lolium perenne* cv. S24 (sown at a rate of 50kg ha⁻¹) and *Festuca tenuifolia* (sown at 30kg ha⁻¹) were much less successful, either for stabilisation or as companion species.

The reasons for these differences in performance are:
1)   *A. castellana* seedlings established quite rapidly and formed a prostrate, loosely tillered and open sward with consistent ground cover. This sward produced a favourable micro-environment for the

germination, establishment and growth of *Calluna* and *Erica* spp, probably due to increased humidity at and near the ground surface.

2) *L. perenne* requires high mineral nutrient availability on neutral to moderately acid soils. The experimental mineral nutrient input was insufficient to sustain *Lolium*, and there were severe visual symptoms of nutrient deficiency probably exacerbated by the low soil pH. Two years after sowing most of the *L.perenne* had died out.

3) *Festuca tenuifolia* was slow to establish and grow. Many individual plants eventually became well-established and formed dense tufts, but well spaced out. The relatively large gaps between individuals did not provide suitable establishment microsites for heather seedlings.

In another experiment at Lee Moor, the performances of *Agrostis castellana* and *A. vinealis* were compared. The growth of *A. vinealis* was less than *A. castellana*, and the former species was less competitive. The eventual establishment (after five years) of *Calluna* and *Erica* spp. was greater on the *A. vinealis* plots. The autumn colouration of *A. vinealis* was a rich brown which blended well with the surrounding moorland landscape.

One other useful role of these two *Agrostis* species was suppression of establishment of *Juncus effusus* and *J. squarrosus* (both very undesirable), particularly with high fertiliser input. Control plots not sown with the companion species contained large populations of *Juncus*.

The work at Robinson's Moss, Longdendale, Derbyshire (section 2.2.2) demonstrated the value of selected grasses both for stabilising the soil surface, and for providing suitable conditions for the germination of heathland plants.

The results of small-plot experiments established in 1980 are given in Table 3.2.   *Lolium perenne* cv. S 23 and the hybrid cv. Augusta

Table 3.2   Sown commercial cultivars at Robinson's Moss, Derbyshire.
             Effectiveness of species and cultivars for stabilisation of
             bare peat and as companion/nurse species.

Species	Sowing rate kg ha^{-1}	Stabilising performance	Companion nurse species role	Rate of disappearance
Agrostis castellana cv. Highland	17	good	good	moderately persistent, < 5% after 5 years
Festuca rubra cv. S59	1.5 & 22.5	good with high fertiliser + lime	poor, too competitive	moderately fast, <2% after 5 years
Deschampsia flexuosa	30	poor at first but good after 3 yrs	moderately good	very persistent
Lolium perenne cv S23	1.5 & 22.5	satisfactory in first year	poor	fast, <2% after 3 years
L.perenne x multi-florum cv. Augusta	22.5	satisfactory in first year	very poor	fast, <2% after 2 years
Poa pratensis cv. Prato	22.5	poor	poor	moderately fast, <2% after 4 years
Hordeum sativum (spring barley)	–	good in the first year, persistent culms stabilise during winter	–	fast, plants die after 4 months but culms persist longer

provided good stabilisation of peat with high inputs of fertiliser and lime.   However, dense growth of other species in the seed mixtures (*Festuca rubra* cv. S59 and *A. castellana* cv Highland) was encouraged, thus preventing the establishment of *Calluna* and other native species. The optimum approach was establishment of a mixture of *A. castellana* and *D. flexuosa*.   *A. castellana* established reasonably rapidly, and effectively stabilised peat surfaces, whilst the slower growing *D. flexuosa* gradually ousted *A. castellana* to become the dominant species after three to five years. The *Agrostis/ Deschampsia* mixture fulfilled well the nurse/companion species role.

On very unstable areas, sowing *Hordeum sativum* (barley) with *D. flexuosa* and *A. castellana* was a satisfactory method of stabilising peat without causing excessive competition to native species.   Also, in the experiments in the North York Moors National Park, *Avena fatua* (wild oat) was sown as a stabilising plant.   This species is tolerant of soil acidity and low nutrient levels, and performed well.   Wild oat could provide a good alternative to spring barley.

The conclusions concerning species performance on mineral substrates at Robinson's Moss were essentially the same as for peat. However, the seed rates and fertiliser input should be reduced for mineral areas, as the grass vegetation proved more competitive and less native species became established.

The lessons learned from the small plots at Robinson's Moss were applied on a larger scale. An area of 200m^2 bare peat and a similar sized area on a millstone grit substrate were sown with a mixture of *A. castellana* cv Highland (20kg ha^{-1}) and *D. flexuosa* (40kg ha^{-1}). *Secale cereale* (rye) was also sown (50kg ha^{-1}), but failed to establish.   Fertiliser input was ICI No. 5 at 200kg ha^{-1}, with superphosphate at 100kg ha^{-1} and crushed limestone at 2,500kg ha^{-1}. These larger areas have been stabilised effectively, and *Calluna* is colonising the grassland vegetation by seed dispersed from clumps which were transplanted as small plants grown in paper tubes.

On an even larger scale, *D. flexuosa* and *A. castellana* cv. Highland were sown on bare peat in areas of the North York Moors National Park which had been burnt and severely eroded in places (section 2.5.2.). The sowing rates were less than those used at Robinson's Moss, and the associated inputs of crushed limestone and fertiliser were less. However, by the autumn of the second growing season, a good cover of grasses was obtained, and a moderate density of *Calluna* seedlings had appeared on areas where cut heather shoots had been spread.

The same approach was used in the Peak District at Holme Moss (Tallis & Yalden, 1983). *A. castellana* cv. Highland and *D. flexuosa* were each sown at a rate of 3kg ha^{-1} with the addition of heather litter (>600kg ha^{-1} wet weight), fertiliser and hydrated lime. Within two growing seasons, the grass sward was established and there was adequate *Calluna* colonisation.

On lowland sites too, grasses can stabilise surfaces and encourage establishment of heathland species. Details of the seed mixture and the lay-out of treatments used at Pystock Wood (Farnborough), are given in section 3.5.1. Two years after sowing, results showed that *A. castellana* was the most successful over the range of fertiliser and limestone treatments. *Festuca rubra* became well-established on high fertiliser plus lime treatments. The remaining species made only a small contribution to vegetation cover.

The restoration work at Cannock Chase (section 2.5.2) showed that on the more drought prone and acid substrates at Ansons Bank, *A. castellana* cv. Highland performed well, as did *F. rubra* ssp *commutata* cv. Cascade. Otherwise the native species, i.e. *F. tenuifolia, F. ovina* and *D. flexuosa*, established and grew best.

On a less acid, slightly more fertile soil at Milford Common, *A. castellana* cv. Highland performed well as did *F. rubra* spp *commutata* cv. Highlight and cv. Cascade. All *F. rubra* ssp *rubra* cultivars performed poorly. The main conclusion was that *F. rubra* ssp *commutata* was a very suitable companion grass for dry lowland heath areas.

One important facet of sown companion grass species is that they should
eventually die out, leaving the restored area wholly with indigenous
heathland species. There is clear evidence of a progressive decline in
the percentage contribution of *A. castellana* at Lee Moor in Devon
seven years after the experiment was commenced, with an average percent
cover of *Agrostis* of <2% in all plots. A similar decline was
recorded at Robinson's Moss. Sown *L. perenne* had completely
disappeared after two years, *F.rubra* ssp *litoralis* (cv S59) had
vitually gone after four years and *A. castellana* cv. Highland was
reduced to a low percent cover, rarely exceeding 5% and usually <2%
after five years.

3.6.2 Recommended companion grass species

Grasses that are suitable as companion species are listed in Table 3.3.
Their characteristics can be matched to the particular requirements of
different sites. Usually a mixture of different species will be
required to provide initial stabilisation of the soil surface and also a
low-competitive grassland vegetation into which native heathland species
(especially the heathers) can colonise. Suggested seed mixtures are
described in Appendix II.

Good stabilising properties may be more important in upland heath than
in lowland sites. Possession of rhizomes can be most useful in upland
situations. In lowland dry heath, drought tolerance and tolerance of low
soil fertility will be crucial. Since addition of fertiliser and crushed
limestone may be necessary to assist rapid seedling establishment and
therefore stabilisation, low competitive aggressiveness may be important,
in such circumstances.

Agrostis curtisii and *Molinia caerulea* are included in Table 3.3
but they are not available from seed merchants. Seed of these two
species could be harvested from suitable areas in mid-summer using a
forage harvester. *Agrostis curtisii* would be particularly useful
for restoration of dry/humid heath sites in Dorset, Hampshire and south
west Britain. *Molinia caerulea* would be useful for restoration of
wet heath areas.

Not only are particular species important as components of the heathland restoration process but particular cultivars of some species can also be recommended where they have performed well in experimental or large-scale restoration (see Table 3.4). Cultivars of some species will not always remain available, but there may be alternatives with suitable growth characteristics. The seed suppliers will be able to advise.

3.6.3 Conclusions

1)   Grass companion species are necessary for restoration of upland heath where substrates are eroded. Until an eroding substrate has been stabilised and a sheltered micro-environment created, establishment of heather seedlings will not occur.

2)   There is experimental proof of the beneficial effects of companion species on the seedling establishment of heathers. Most work has been on upland sites, but relevant evidence from lowland heaths also suggests that grass companion species would be useful in restoration. Sowing densities should be lower than for the upland heaths, and it may be necessary to restrict fertiliser input. A mixture of companion grass species seed could include native heathland grasses such as *Deschampsia flexuosa* or *Agrostis curtisii*.

3)   Several suitable species and cultivars of grasses have been identified as being particularly useful in the restoration of heathland. In upland sites, *A. castellana* cv. Highland and *D.flexuosa* have proved most effective as companion species. *A. castellana* is also effective in lowland sites. *D. flexuosa* however is not always a natural component of lowland vegetation and would be inappropriate. In these cases, less is known about the effectiveness of other grass species.

4)   Despite the significance of *A. curtisii* for heathland restoration in Dorset and other areas in south and south-west Britain, commercial seed supplies are not available. It would be worth making arrangements with a seedhouse to bulk-up supplies of *A. curtisii* seed.

Table 3.3. Recommended companion grass species and their main characteristics which are significant for restoration of heathland

Species	Rapidity of establish-ment.	Competitive aggressive-ness	Usefulness as a stabiliser	Presence of rhizomes	Drought toler-ance	Suitability for wet heath	Tolerance of low soil fertility	Requirement for fertil-iser & ground limestone
Deschampsia flexuosa	slow	moderate	poor but improves	no	moderate	yes	good	low/moderate
Festuca ovina/tenuifolia	slow	low	poor	no	good	no	good	moderate
Festuca longifolia	slow/ moderate	low/ moderate	moderate	no	good	no	moderate/ good	moderate/ low
Festuca rubra ssp commutata ‡	slow/ moderate	moderate	moderate	no	good	no	moderate	moderate
Festuca rubra ssp litoralis	moderate	moderate/ high	moderate/ good	yes	moderate	no	moderate/ poor	moderate/ low
Agrostis castellana	moderate	moderate/ low	moderate/ good	yes	moderate	qualified	moderate	moderate
*Agrostis curtisii**	slow	low	poor	no	good	no	good	low
Agrostis vinealis = A.canina ssp montana ‡	slow	low	poor	no	moderate	no	good	low/moderate
Agrostis canina = A.canina ssp canina‡	slow/ moderate	moderate	moderate/ poor	creeping stolons	moderate/ low	yes	moderate	moderate
*Molinia caerulea**	moderate	moderate/ high	moderate	no	poor	yes	moderate	low/moderate
Lolium perenne	rapid	high	good	no	poor	no	low	high

* not available commercially

‡ nomenclature according to Hubbard, 1968.

Table 3.4   **Cultivars of grass companion species which should be**
           suitable for heathland restoration

Species	Cultivars
Festuca ovina/tenuifolia	Barok*, Novina
Festuca longifolia	Scaldis, Tournament*, Biljart*
Festuca rubra ssp *commutata*‡	Highlight, Rasengold,* Cascade
Festuca rubra ssp *litoralis*	Aberystwyth S59, Pennlawn*
Festuca rubra ssp *pruinosa*	Merlin
Agrostis castellana	Highland
Agrostis capillaris	
(=*A.tenuis*)‡	Tracenta*
Agrostis vinealis	
(=*A.canina* ssp *montana*)‡	Novobent*, Kingston*
Lolium perenne	Aberystwyth S23, Augusta (Hybrid)

‡ nomenclature according to Hubbard, 1968

* these cultivars have not been evaluated for heathland restoration,
  but may be suitable as their growth characteristics are appropriate.
  Discussion with the seed supplier is recommended.

3.7   Mineral nutrient input and control of substrate pH

3.7.1   Effects of fertiliser and lime on the growth of heathers
        and companion grasses

There are two main reasons why application of mineral nutrients may be
necessary to achieve successful heathland restoration. Firstly, it may
be necessary to ameliorate the pH of very acid substrates in order to
obtain satisfactory growth of sown companion grass species. Since the
sown grasses may have a stabilising role, particularly in eroding upland
areas of heathland, rapid establishment is necessary. Therefore inputs
of major mineral nutrients, particularly of nitrogen and phosphorus,
will also be required.

Secondly, additions of nitrogen and phosphorus may also help seedling
establishment and early growth of *Calluna* and *Erica* spp as well
as native grasses such as *Deschampsia flexuosa* and *Agrostis
curtisii*.

The documented evidence is considerable. For example, Gillham (1980) found that in heath restoration at Lee Moor, Devon, a single initial application of ICI No.5 (17:17:17) at rates of 100 and 300kg ha^{-1}, considerably assisted the establishment of ericoid seedlings, mainly *Calluna*, with the effect still evident after seven years. This was particularly so in plots where *A. castellana* was sown as a companion species (Fig. A1.2 in App.I). Tallis & Yalden (1983), working in the Peak District National Park, also found this to be the case in upland heath/blanket peat. Data in Table 3.5 indicate the very positive influence of the addition of 312kg ha^{-1} hydrated lime, 62.5kg ha^{-1} NPK fertiliser (17:17:17) and 15.6kg h^{-1} superphosphate. Helsper *et al.* (1983) carried out a turf cutting and fertilisation experiment on a *Calluna*-dominated lowland heath in the Netherlands. Regeneration of *Calluna* from the soil seed pool was enhanced by a single application of nitrogen ($NH_4.NO_3$., 86kg ha^{-1}) at the start of the experiment. However, not surprisingly, repeated applications in subsequent years caused suppression of *Calluna* by other species.

Table 3.5   The influence of fertiliser on the establishment of heather seedlings from litter. Holme Moss, Derbyshire, May 1981-Sept 1982. (after Tallis & Yalden, 1983)

Treatment		Fenced	Unfenced
Bare peat[1]	: Fertilised	110	70
	: Unfertilised	36	19
Mineral substrate[2]	: Fertilised	28	1
	: Unfertilised	0	0

[1]   Numbers of plants per 0.4m^2

[2]   Numbers of plants per 8m^2

Gillham (1980) also carried out experiments where *Calluna vulgaris* and *Erica tetralix* were grown on china clay sand waste (from Lee Moor, Devon), with and without other heathland species (mainly grasses, with *Molinia caerulea* as the most abundant species). In the absence

of other species, there was an increase in heather biomass with
application of mineral nutrients (NPK) up to 25kg ha^{-1} of each element
(applied together). A factorial experiment showed that maximum heather
biomass was obtained by addition of phosphorus alone, or nitrogen and
phosphorus. With competition from other species, applications of 12.5
and 25.0kg ha^{-1} of NPK gave similar biomass yields, but higher rates of
50, 100 and 200kg ha^{-1} gave a progressive reduction in heather biomass
down to a very small value. *Calluna* and *Erica tetralix* were
clearly very sensitive to competition from other species at higher
levels of mineral nutrient input.

The extensive experiments at Robinson's Moss also provided useful data
on the significance of mineral nutrient input for heathland restoration
on upland acid peat substrates. Details of fertiliser treatments are
given in Tables A1.2 and A1.3, Appendix I. In May 1981, one year after
the initial application, certain plots were given additional fertiliser.
Each plot was halved into two equal sub-plots and one half received
fertiliser at one half the rate which was originally applied in May
1980.

Progress was monitored for five years, and the following conclusions
were drawn:

1)   After two years, there was no establishment of *A. castellana*,
      D.flexuosa or *Calluna* on *any* plot which had not
      received fertiliser or limestone.

2)   After five years, there was *very limited* establishment (< 10%
      cover) only of *D. flexuosa* on some of the "no fertiliser"
      plots.

3)   The initial application of fertiliser and limestone generally
      enhanced the establishment and growth of *Calluna* when
      measured after 2, 3, 4 and 5 years.

4)   The additional fertiliser treatment (May 1981) generally
      suppressed the growth and establishment of *Calluna*
      throughout the five year period.

5)   The additional fertiliser treatment increased the growth of *D. flexuosa* but at the expense of other native heathland species.

6)   The influence of the fertiliser treatments remained very clear five years after the start of the experiment.

Other published data on growth responses of *Calluna* and *D. flexuosa* are given by Gore (1975), who observed that *Calluna* responded to enhanced mineral nutrition at the expense of cotton grass (*E. vaginatum*).   Gore & Godfrey (1981) showed that applications of lime and nitrogen (30kg ha^{-1}) and phosphorus (100kg ha^{-1}) were necessary for the successful establishment and growth of *D. flexuosa* on bare, eroded blanket peat in the Pennines (cf. Robinson's Moss), and Miles (1974) demonstrated that on a peaty podzol soil there was a significant response in the growth of *Calluna* to addition of nitrogen and phosphate.

On acid peat deficient in mineral nutrients, or on mineral soils typical of the majority of upland and lowland heaths, it is usually impossible to establish companion grass species without addition of fertiliser and often lime as well, at levels which will suppress the establishment of heathers and other native heathland species.   Also, different companion grass species have different requirements for germination.   For example, at Lee Moor, Gillham (1980) found that *F. rubra* cv. S59 required at least 2,500kg ha^{-1} ground limestone plus 300kg ha^{-1} NPK fertiliser (17:17:17) for successful establishment and maintenance for one year. *Agrostis castellana* and *Festuca ovina* required 300kg ha^{-1} ICI No.5, but established without addition of lime.   At Pant-yr-Dwr, Powys, on an upland site with peaty podzol and deep peat soils, satisfactory establishment and subsequent growth of *L. perenne* cv. S23, *F. rubra* cv. S59, *Phleum pratense* and *Lolium* hybrid 'Augusta' required 250kg ha^{-1} nitrogen, 100-125kg ha^{-1} phosphorus and 80-100kg ha^{-1} potassium (Munro *et al.*,1972).

Thus for practical purposes, acid tolerant species such as *A. castellana* and *D. flexuosa* are the most appropriate companion species to use in restoration of upland or lowland heath.

3.7.2   Conclusions

There is considerable evidence to demonstrate the necessity for input of mineral nutrients for successful restoration of heathland vegetation on most types of heathland soils. However, there is a relatively delicate balance between applying sufficient fertiliser and too much. Non-grass heathland species (including heather) are very sensitive to competition from the grass component of the vegetation, and excessive input of mineral nutrients will increase grass growth too much.

On some lowland heaths, soil fertility may be somewhat greater than in acid peat upland heaths. This is reflected in the fact that oak woodland would ultimately develop on such areas if they were left undisturbed for a sufficient length of time (e.g. Cannock Chase). In lowland heath sites considerably more caution must be exercised over input of mineral nutrients. Ideally, preliminary fertiliser trials should be carried out before any major programme of heathland restoration is attempted.

3.8   Shelter materials, forestry brashings and chemical stabilisers

Heathland restoration cannot proceed until eroding substrates have been stabilised sufficiently to allow establishment of native heathland species, and also in very exposed sites, to assist the establishment of companion grass species. Companion grasses (section 3.6) are an important means of providing surface stabilisation and sheltered microsites for the establishment of heather seedlings. However, where a dense grass sward has developed, particularly on lowland heath sites (eg Cannock Chase) and where soil fertility is not an extreme limiting factor, companion grasses may actually prevent seedling establishment of heathers and other native heathland species. Each site proposed for heathland restoration has to be assessed for susceptibility to erosion but there are many sites where the use of forestry brashings or shelter materials, such as cut heather stems, may be either a superior alternative to the use of sown companion grasses or complementary to the sowing of slow-growing native heathland grasses (e.g. *Deschampsia flexuosa, Festuca ovina, F. tenuifolia* and *Agrostis curtisii*).   In some situations, chemical stabilisers may also be useful.

3.8.1   The use of forestry brashings

Larch forestry brashings were used in experiments in the Peak District National Park (section 2.4.2).

At Burbage Moor and Cabin Clough, fenced and unfenced plots were established and spread with cut heather shoots, with and without larch brashings.

The data in Table 3.6 show that at Burbage Moor, the larch brashings increased the establishment of *Calluna* by 2.9 times in the fenced area.   Percent cover was increased by approximately the same amount. The impact of the larch treatment was also substantial in the unfenced area, although the effect had diminished by the end of the third growing season (Tallis & Yalden, 1983).   At Cabin Clough, the larch treatment was effective only within the fenced area.

Forestry brashings have also been used very successfully for restoration of eroded lowland heath areas at Cannock Chase Country Park (Countryside Commission, 1985), and for restoration of upland grass heath at Moel Famau Country Park, Clwydian Hills, North Wales (Thompson, pers. comm. 1986).   At both places, the primary objective was restoration of grass-dominated vegetation on severely trampled areas and eroded slopes. Establishment of species such as *Agrostis capillaris* and *Festuca ovina* was excellent and at Cannock Chase was more successful than establishment in fenced-off areas which did not have the brashings treatment.   These results indicate that establishment of grass companion species on exposed sites or areas subject to surface erosion or surface disturbance would be considerably assisted by the use of forestry brashings.   Other native heathland species, particularly heather, could be introduced once the grasses had become established.

3.8.2   The use of chemical stabilisers

Practical experience indicates that although some stabiliser products may be useful for a period of a few weeks and allow establishment of fast growing grasses, they are not effective for long enough to assist the slower growing native grasses, or *Calluna*.

Table 3.6   **The mean* number of *Calluna* plants and percent cover of**
Calluna per 4 x 4m plot at two sites in Derbyshire
(compiled from Tallis & Yalden, 1983)

Treatment	Site		
	Burbage Moor		Cabin Clough
	Number of heather plants 26.3.82	Percent cover of heather 30.8.82	Number of heather plants 31.8.82
Heather only:			
Fenced	199.0	14.3	4.7
Unfenced	68.7	4.7	25.0
Heather plus larch brashings:			
Fenced	586.7	42.7	185.3
Unfenced	202.7	7.7	17.0

*   Mean of 3 replicate plots

Where deep peats or peaty podzol soils are concerned, Johnson
(pers.comm.1981) suggests that resin and polyvinyl stabilisers (e.g.
Vinamul) would be unable to cope with a granular material of low bulk
density.   Roberts & Bradshaw (1985) investigated the efficacy of a
variety of stabilisers in binding a coarse mineral waste (china clay sand
waste) after hydraulic seeding, and found that a wide range of
formulations failed to improve plant establishment.   Some formulations
were ineffective in binding sand grains, and actually decreased plant
establishment.   Unisol and Essbinder were particularly poor.

Three types of chemical stabiliser were tested by the EAU on two
substrates at Robinson's Moss.   One substrate was a sloping bare peat
surface, and the other a sloping mineral area with larger boulders and
smaller fragments of millstone grit with some peat in crevices.

Three stabilisers were applied (or not) in September 1980, in combination with companion grass species, fertiliser and crushed limestone. The stabilisers were:

> Alginure granulate S - an alginate material capable of forming a
>   thixotropic gel.
>
> Verdyol complex   - an organic colloid material
>
> Curasol AH   - a chemical glue

Establishment of companion grasses was assessed in May 1981, after a winter period when severe climatic conditions and consequent erosion provided a useful test of stabiliser performance. Selected data are shown in Table 3.He stabilisers had given some increased establishment of *Agrostis castellana*, but overall performance was poor. Total vegetation cover was low on even the best of the stabiliser -treated plots. A drawback with Verdyol complex and Curasol AH was that although a stabilised crust formed, particularly on peat, once the surface became cracked or penetrated, the whole crust would rapidly break down and erode.

The Moorland Restoration Project in the Peak District National Park used a bitumen-based stabiliser, 'Bitumuls', at Burbage Moor and Cabin Clough. The results at Burbage Moor were the most informative because this site had the greatest number of *Calluna* seedlings and also quite good establishment of other species. Within fenced areas, the application of Bitumuls (in comparison with control plots) increased the number of established heather plants by a factor of 1.7 - 2.1, and the total plant cover at the end of three growing seasons by a factor of 1.5. However, to put this in context, although the use of Bitumuls was clearly beneficial, in general, the use of larch brashings gave rather better establishment of *Calluna* and better total plant cover.

At Cabin Clough, the Bitumuls treatment was slightly effective within the fenced area, but gave many fewer established heather plants than did forestry brashings. In the unfenced area, the Bitumuls treatment gave worse results than in the control plots where cut heather shoots only were spread, without chemical stabiliser treatment.

Table 3.7 **Establishment of** *A. castellana* **in plots treated with**
chemical stabilisers at Robinson's Moss.

Site	Chemical stabiliser	Percent cover *A. castellana*
Sloping bare peat	Alginure +	14.7
	Alginure −	5.3
	Verdyol +	11.3
	Verdyol −	4.3
	Curasol +	8.7
	Curasol −	7.0
Sloping mineral area	Alginure +	8.7
	Alginure −	9.7
	Verdyol +	8.0
	Verdyol −	0.0
	Curasol +	3.7
	Curasol −	0.0

The National Trust has commenced a programme of restoration of *Calluna*
vegetation on bare eroding blanket peat at Kinder Scout, Derbyshire.
This involves spreading cut heather shoots bearing seed capsules and
sowing of *Deschampsia flexuosa* and *Agrostis castellana*, with
some input of fertiliser and crushed limestone. Erodofix, a rubber
emulsion product, had some effect in binding of peat over the first
winter, but in the longer-term had little effect on the development of a
vegetation cover.

Meaden (1983) carried out some very limited laboratory tests of three
stabilisers, Curasol AH, Curasol AE and Dunebond. On sand substrates,
Dunebond gave the longest lasting stabilisation of the sand surface.

However, tests with *Calluna*, *A. castellana* and *F. longifolia*
showed that Dunebond suppressed the germination of all three species.
Meaden concluded that none of the stabilisers tested would be
particularly useful in heathland restoration.

3.8.3   Conclusions

Most testing of chemical stabilisers has been in upland heath areas.
The useful stabilising effects are relatively short-term, and then
sites probably require protection from grazing animals. Even in upland
areas, forestry brashings have proved to be a more effective means of
providing shelter for establishing seedlings of *Calluna* and other
native heathland species.

The role of chemical stabilisers in the restoration of lowland heath is
even less clear-cut. In this environment, there appears to be an even
stronger case for the use of forestry brashings, cut heather shoots or
other shelter materials such as 'Geojute'.

4.0 EARLY AFTERCARE AND MANAGEMENT

Heathland restoration is not a one-off event. It is a *whole process*
which requires some commitment to aftercare and management in the early
years following initial restoration. The restored area may need to be
protected from grazing animals, and the developing heathland may
require some management to ensure a vegetation with a well-balanced
species content. There will normally be a dominance of *Calluna*
and *Erica* spp, but with representation by other typical heathland
species appropriate to upland or lowland sites.

4.1 Mineral nutrient input

During the initial phase of heathland restoration, there will have been
an input of mineral nutrient elements appropriate to the characteristics
of the site (section 3.7). Whether or not further applications are
necessary is questionable. Soil fertility must remain sufficiently low
to ensure that any sown companion grass species will die out within a
few years.   Furthermore, other native grasses must not become too
abundant.   This would be encouraged by excessive input of mineral
nutrients in the long-term (Heil & Diemont, 1983; Helsper *et al.*
1983).

4.1.1   The significance of mineral nutrient input after the first year

Experiments carried out for CEGB at Robinson's Moss by the EAU included
in the design an additional input of NPK fertiliser during the second
year after initial treatment.   The acid peat substrate was very
deficient in mineral nutrients, so an additional input of nutrients was
made to determine whether or not:

- input of further nutrients was necessary to sustain sown companion
  species, and allow continued stabilization of the peat,
- maintenance of a high vegetation cover of grasses would adversely
  affect the growth of native heathland species.

Existing plots were halved, and one half (randomly selected) received
100kg ha^{-1} ICI No.5 fertiliser and 50kg ha^{-1} of superphosphate.   This
was half the original application rate in the first year.

After three years, it was clear that the additional input of mineral
nutrients had increased the growth of the grasses, particularly
Deschampsia flexuosa, and that this had reduced the establishment and
growth of several native heathland species.   *Calluna* in particular
was adversely affected, although in certain sites without companion
grasses, growth of *Calluna* was satisfactory in the plots which had
received the additional nutrient input (Table 4.1).

Table 4.1 **The effect of additional mineral nutrients applied in the
second year on percentage frequency of *Calluna***

Site	One initial application only		Additional application in year two	
(Robinson's Moss)	With companion grass	Without companion grass	With companion grass	Without companion grass
Mineral area	–	13	3	25
Level peat	33	16	1	24
Sloping peat	48	31	28	1
Peat lagoon	16	40	7	3

Plate 17. Successful regeneration (after three years six months) of turves placed adjacent to the Welsh Water Authority office at Llyn Brenig.

Plate 18. An area of former lowland heath in Surrey which has been graded with a bulldozer after clearance of scrub.

At Lee Moor in South Devon, the heathland restoration experiment (section 2.1.2 and App 1(1.1)) was left undisturbed for a period of five years. Then all plots received an application of Enmag fertiliser (at a rate of 100kg ha^{-1}). Although this treatment did not involve a critical comparison since there were no untreated plots, there was a noticeable improvement in the growth of *Calluna* and *Erica* spp over the following two years. There is no certainty that this was the result of Enmag treatment, but the evidence is strongly circumstantial. This correlates with the findings of Gillham (1980) that a combination of nitrogen and phosphate (but particularly phosphate) at moderate application rates improved the growth of *Calluna*.

There is also some evidence that older stands of heather will respond to fertiliser input. Miller (1979) and Miller *et al.*(1970) found that nitrogen input (e.g ammonium nitrate at 105 kg ha^{-1} of nitrogen) substantially improved the growth of upland heather, but that addition of phosphate fertiliser did not. On the other hand, Watson & O'Hare (1979) found that a massive input of phosphate fertiliser on blanket peat in Western Ireland increased growth of heather. Input was 502kg ha^{-1} of ground mineral phosphate (14.5%P).

4.1.2   Conclusions

Although the evidence is somewhat fragmentary and inconclusive, it appears that on substrates which are very deficient in mineral nutrients, additional input of nitrogen and phosphorus in combination may improve the growth of heather. Application should be several years after the initial restoration, and the use of a slow release product with a relatively high phosphorus content is recommended. Enmag (6N, 20 P$_2$O$_5$, 10K$_2$O) would appear to be a suitable fertiliser for this purpose.

4.2   Control of undesirable species using herbicides

After an initial heather restoration programme has been completed the developing heathland vegetation cannot necessarily be left to its own devices. Particularly in lowland heaths, rapid succession to scrub woodland is a possibility because seed of gorse, birch or pine may have been introduced (in soil or litter or turves) as a component of the dormant seed pool. The potential problem may be less acute where cut heather shoots have been used as the source of heather propagules. Invasion by bracken, grasses and excessively high populations of *Ulex* spp are other potential problems that may have to be tackled.

In relatively small-scale restoration, and in the early stages of vegetation development, labour intensive hand-pulling will control young birch and pine. Cutting will also control pine, but not birch, which regenerates from cut stumps. On a larger scale, and where trees are older, spraying of individuals or cutting followed by herbicide treatment of stumps will be the most effective means of scrub control.

4.2.1 Legislation on the use of herbicides

The legislation regarding the use of pesticides (including herbicides) is undergoing change, with many new restrictions being phased in over a period of time. It is essential therefore that anyone contemplating the use of herbicides should be familiar with The Control of Pesticides Regulations 1986, which are a set of requirements made under the Food and Environment Protection Act 1985.

To date, the most relevant requirements are that only "approved" products can be used (see Pesticides 1988, or The UK Pesticides Guide 1988), and that users must be competent and have received adequate instruction and guidance in the safe, efficient and humane use of pesticides. As from 1 January '88, it is also necessary for anyone who sells, supplies or stores approved pesticides to have a certificate of competence, and for all users to comply with the conditions of approval relating to use.   These uses will be clearly stated either on the product label or in the published approval for the pesticide. Matters covered will include: protective clothing, use on certain crops, type of situation and who can use the products, maximum rates, minimum harvest intervals, bee protection, control of access after treatment, etc. From 1 January 1989, contractors using pesticides will be required to hold certificates of competence, as will anyone born after 31 December 1964.

A useful synopsis of the situation at the time of writing is given by
Bannister (1987). Essential reference books are:

-   "Pesticides 1988" produced by the Ministry of Agriculture,
    Fisheries and Food and the Health and Safety Executive. Available
    from HMSO.

-   "The UK Pesticides Guide 1988" produced by the Commonwealth
    Agricultural Bureaux and the British Crop Protection Council.

-   "Pesticides. Code of Practice for the Use of Approved Pesticides
    in Amenity Areas" 1987, produced by the National Turfgrass Council
    and the National Association of Agricultural Contractors.

4.2.2 Treatment of woody species with herbicide sprays

There is an effective range of herbicides available for the control of
woody weeds, and their use for heathland management has been thoroughly
tested and reviewed (Marrs, 1983a; 1984a; 1984b; 1985).

There is a marked reluctance by conservationists to use herbicides,
which is unfortunate because they are a powerful tool for the management
of vegetation (Harper 1971; Marrs 1983b).   There are understandable
fears that chemicals for controlling weed species may also be toxic to
non-target organisms, or leave residues in the soil and in the biota.
These fears are probably due to our lack of understanding that
herbicides are generally less persistent in the environment than, for
example, insecticides, and to our poor knowledge of the tolerance of
native plants and animals to them. However a suitable herbicide should
be included in the management strategy of heathlands, if efficient and
cost-effective control of deciduous scrub species is to be achieved.

The questions that should be considered before contemplating the use of
herbicides are:

•   are appropriate herbicides available?
•   Has the herbicide received approval for use as a control for woody
    species in an amenity/conservation context?
•   are there any deleterious effects on non-target organisms?

- how can the herbicide be applied easily for maximum benefit and with minimum damage?
- are competent trained personnel available to apply the herbicides (section 4.2.5)

Some herbicides suitable for control of woody species in heathlands as foliar sprays or cut stump treatments are:

a) **Ammonium sulphamate** can be used as a foliar spray, or applied (either as crystals or in solution) to cut stumps. This herbicide is non-selective, and thus cannot be used as a general foliar spray as there is potential damage to non-target plants. This problem is avoided if it is applied to cut stumps. This chemical is marketed as "Amcide" by Battle, Hayward & Bower Ltd.

b) **Fosamine ammonium** is used as a foliar spray. It should be sprayed in late August or September before the leaves fall.
    It is marketed by Du Pont (UK) Ltd as 'Krenite'.

c) **Triclopyr** is suitable for foliar spraying of small trees, and for stump application. It is manufactured as 'Garlon 4' by Chipman Ltd. Although efficient for birch control, it may cause some damage to *Calluna vulgaris* (Marrs & Lowday, 1981).

d) **Glyphosate** is a non-selective translocated herbicide. It can be applied as a spray, or 'wiped' onto target plants directly. It is also useful as a stump treatment for controlling woody weeds. Glyphosate is marketed as 'Roundup' by Monsanto plc and as 'Spasor' by May & Baker Agrochemicals.

e) **Hexazinone** is a non-selective, residual, translocated herbicide which is primarily taken up through the roots. It controls many grasses and some broad-leaved weeds, and can be useful as a stump treatment for woody species. Du Pont (UK) Ltd supplies this chemical as 'Velpar'.

The addresses of these suppliers are given in Appendix III.

When applied as a foliar spray, fosamine ammonium caused little damage to heathland vegetation (Marrs, 1984b). Triclopyr caused some damage to *Calluna*, and is recommended for use on grass heath only as a general spray (Marrs & Lowday, 1981). Triclopyr is particularly effective as a directed spray for control of gorse (*Ulex europaeus*), especially when applied in July or September.

4.2.3   Treatment of cut stumps

Since many herbicides which will control woody species will also damage desirable non-target heathland species, their use must be confined to treatment of cut stumps by direct application after cutting. This treatment is particularly useful for the control of birch (Marrs, 1985a). Marrs tested several herbicides at different times of the year. He found that for cut stump treatments, fosamine ammonium, triclopyr and glyphosate were effective all year round. Ammonium sulphamate was best applied in winter, spring and summer, whereas hexazinone was most effective in winter and spring.

The only drawbacks to stump treatments are firstly, that rainfall immediately after treatment may wash the herbicide off the stumps and thus reduce its effectiveness, and secondly, that effective treatment depends on treating a stump within 24 hours of cutting.

4.2.4   Treatment of bracken

Invasion by bracken may be a problem on recently restored burnt areas of heathland, and occasionally on pipeline routes, but it is less likely to be a problem in heathland restored after mineral extraction or major construction work.

On established heathland it is possible to control bracken by regular annual cutting. For example, on an area of Breckland in East Anglia, Lowday (1983) showed that cutting stands of bracken in mid-June, and again in late July for four consecutive years, decreased above-ground biomass to 1% of uncut areas. Bracken should be cut in mid-June to late

July when rhizome reserves are low. Daniels (1983) has argued that cutting twice per year is unnecessary, and reports that at Cannock Chase bracken was severely weakened by cutting once per year for four years.

There is considerable experience of the control of bracken in established heathland using the herbicide asulam, which is marketed as "Asulox" by May and Baker Ltd. (Marrs & Lowday, 1981; Lowday, 1983, 1984a, 1984b; Countryside Commission, 1985). The general consensus appears to be that asulam applied once in July when fronds are fully expanded will give a 95% reduction in frond density in the following year (Lowday, 1983), although experience at Cannock Chase suggests 88-93% reduction (Countryside Commission, 1985). Daniels also found that respraying asulam in five successive years gave the best bracken control but did not eradicate it. Daniels recommends that optimum control is achieved by spraying asulam in year 1, cutting in years 2, 3 and 4 and spraying asulam again in year 5.

Recent experimental work (O'Connor, Flint & Aquilina, 1987; Williams & Davies, 1987) has shown that a mixture of the sulphonyl-urea herbicides, chlorsulfuron and metsulfuron-methyl gave effective control of bracken with little damage to the species present in the underlying swards. The sulphonyl-urea herbicides are considerably cheaper than asulam, but are not yet approved for the control of bracken, although one, "Finesse" manufactured by Du Pont, is approved for agricultural use on cereals.

In restored areas of heathland, control of bracken should be required rarely, and even then it is unlikely to be dense enough for cutting to be feasible. Small areas of bracken can be treated with herbicide using a knapsack sprayer.

4.2.5   Control of grasses using herbicides and growth retardants

There are two kinds of situation where grass-killing herbicides or grass growth-retarding chemicals would be useful in a programme of heathland restoration. The first is where heathland has naturally become dominated by grasses, and the second is for control of sown companion grasses. The first situation arises as a result of excessive grazing (e.g. in upland heaths in particular, such as the Clwydian Hills and the

Peak District), trampling pressure (e.g. in many southern lowland heaths), or after severe fire when grasses have re-colonised more rapidly than heathers and have become dominant (e.g. in parts of Cannock Chase). Under these circumstances, competition from the grasses is the main reason why heather seedlings fail to establish, and why existing plants fail to grow satisfactorily. Selective herbicides could suppress grass growth sufficiently to allow improved growth and eventual dominance of *Calluna* and *Erica* spp.

Because of the reluctance by conservationists to use herbicides, there is little practical evidence of the way in which grass-killing herbicides could be used effectively. The only information available is on the use of dalapon by the National Trust on lowland heath sites in Surrey. At Headley Heath near Box Hill, this chemical was applied with a knap-sack sprayer onto degenerate areas of grass heath. *Calluna* was not seriously damaged by the dalapon, and increased growth and colonisation by *Calluna* followed its use. Dalapon is marketed by several companies including Atlas Interlates Ltd, Burts & Harvey, and Battle, Hayward & Bower Ltd.

Herbicides which are selective for grasses will also be useful in reducing or eliminating sown companion grass species. Where the grass (e.g. *Agrostis castellana*) has become too abundant, either because the sowing rate was excessively high, or because soil fertility was sufficient to result in excessive grass growth, selective elimination will be necessary.

Meaden (1983) carried out some small-plot experiments in which mixed *Calluna/A.castellana* vegetation was sprayed with dalapon. The dose rate was 4kg ha^{-1}. The results showed that *A.castellana* was severely checked by dalapon and that *Calluna* was almost unaffected.

In another experiment, several grass species grown in pots in a glass-house were sprayed with dalapon (at the same dose rate as the field experiment). Growth of *Festuca ovina, F. longifolia* and *Deschampsia flexuosa* was only moderately checked by the dalapon treatment. Thus, although the most commonly used companion grass species (*A. castellana*) is susceptible to dalapon, other species are more tolerant, and the effectiveness of dalapon in general field use may be limited.

Meaden also investigated the effects of several other herbicides on *Calluna* (as the non-target species), and four species of grasses (*A. castellana*, *F. longifolia*, *F.ovina* and *D. flexuosa*). Propyzamide, hexazinone, and cyanazine plus atrazine were applied at the recommended dose rate, and caused 75%-99% mortality of *A. castellana* The other grass species were less effectively controlled. Propyzamide was the only herbicide which caused negligible damage to *Calluna*. This herbicide controls a wide range of grass species but it must be applied in winter. The principal marketed products are Kerb granules and Kerb 50 W wettable powder (Pan Britannica Industries Ltd).

Although there is no other known work on the use of selective grass-killing herbicides, two or three other products might be useful in heathland management or restoration, although they have not been tested on a heathland ecosystem. Alloxydim-sodium (marketed as 'Clout' by May & Baker) is a herbicide which controls a wide range of grass species very effectively, and causes little or no damage to many broadleaved herbaceous plants and shrubs. Mefluidide and paclobutrazol are growth-retardant chemicals which slow down the growth of many grass species. At moderate doses, growth completely ceases for three or four months. High doses of mefluidide are phytotoxic, and grass mortality occurs. These chemicals also retard the shoot growth of some shrub and tree species, so tests on *Calluna* and *Erica* spp are required.

4.2.6   Herbicide application methods

It is very easy to mis-apply herbicides. Under the Control of Pesticides Regulations (1986) there is a legal requirement that all personnel responsible for using herbicides are competent in their use, and are properly trained in the calculation of application rates, the methods of application, and the safety precautions that must be taken. From 1 January 1988, herbicides can only be used in the situation for which they have been given approval e.g. agricultural use or for use in amenity areas. As from 1 January 1989, anyone born after 31 December 1964 must hold a certificate of competence for the use of pesticides (section 4.2.1)

a)   Conventional spraying

This includes knapsack sprayers, mist blowers and tractor mounted sprayers. The method selected will relate to the size of the operation and the nature of the terrain.

b)   Herbicide application to cut surfaces

Herbicides can be applied to cut surfaces with paint brushes or hatchet guns. Ammonium sulphamate crystals may be applied directly to cut surfaces.

c)   Basal bark treatment

This technique is not as flexible as application to cut stumps. The herbicide (usually in oil) is sprayed or painted onto the bark at or near ground level. Ammonium sulphamate can be applied as a basal bark treatment.

4.2.7   Conclusions

Extensive invasion by gorse, birch, pine or bracken will detract from the long-term success of any heathland restoration. These species can be controlled effectively by a suite of herbicides which can be applied either as sprays, as basal bark treatments or as cut stump treatments. In some sites, cutting management may be an alternative to treatment with herbicides. It is important that any developing problem of invasion by undesirable species is detected and dealt with early, when herbicide treatment will be less costly, and probably less damaging to non-target heathland species.

At present there is insufficient knowledge about the way in which grass-killing herbicides or growth-retardant chemicals could be effectively used in the management and restoration of heathland, and further research is required on this topic.

In view of the changes in legislation, the reader is reminded that only approved products can be used, and only trained personnel can use them.

4.3   Cutting and grazing management

When the initial programme of heathland restoration has been completed,
disturbance must be avoided for a period of three or four years to allow
heathers and other native species to establish and grow. This will
normally require exclusion of grazing animals, principally large
herbivores. Small mammals appear to be less of a problem. However a
consequence of lack of grazing, particularly in lowland heath sites,
will be establishment of unwanted species, such as *Betula pendula*
and *Betula pubescens* (birch), *Pinus sylvestris* (Scots pine),
Rhododendron ponticum and excessively high populations of *Ulex* spp
(gorse). Scattered patches of gorse will be a necessary component of
many lowland heath ecosystems, but dense and extensive stands will be
undesirable since heather will be suppressed and eventually eliminated.

4.3.1 The practical value of cutting management for recently restored
        heathlands

Cutting management is widely used by conservation organisations as a
means of controlling the ingress of trees, shrubs and bracken (section
4.2.3) on existing mature heathlands, particularly in lowland areas.
Sometimes cutting is carried out in conjunction with herbicide treatment
of cut stumps (section 4.2.2). However, there is less information on
the use of cutting on recently restored areas of heathland.

The successful establishment of lowland heath turves on roadside
embankments near Poole involved cutting management. *Ulex* seedlings
had established on the embankments, presumably because germination had
been encouraged by disturbance, which left seed at or near the soil
surface. Rapid growth of *Ulex* was prevented by regular annual
cutting with a hydraulically operated flail on an extension arm. In
roadside situations, gorse is considered a fire hazard, and control is
essential. In other heathland restoration sites, this would not
necessarily be a problem and such regular cutting management would be
unnecessary.

The National Trust probably has the greatest experience in cutting
management following heathland restoration in Surrey, Hampshire, and
West and East Sussex (Mackworth-Praed, pers.comm. 1980). Cutting has

been used routinely on relatively flat areas of lowland heath which have been restored following encroachment by shrubs, bracken and trees, often after severe fire. Once the areas which are being restored have been cleared and levelled, and colonisation by heathers and other desirable native heath species has commenced, cutting management is undertaken.

The general approach is to cut annually using a tractor-mounted swipe. Height of cut depends on the age of the heather. If cutting is required when heather is young (2-4 years), the cutting height can be 150mm. When the post-restoration age of the heath is 5-10 years, cutting height has been 200-250mm. This has controlled the potential resurgence of bracken very effectively, and has prevented invasion by tree seedlings. The only disadvantage of this method of management would appear to be that it is restricted to relatively level areas where tractor access is possible. Cutting with a flail would cope successfully with undulating topography and steeper slopes.

4.3.2   The importance of protecting recently restored heathland from grazing animals

There is widespread and incontrovertible evidence (already discussed) that grazing by large herbivores (e.g. sheep, horses) reduces the establishment and growth of *Calluna* and *Erica* spp. In recently restored heathland, young heather seedlings are damaged by trampling, and small plants are pulled out of the ground. Protection is therefore essential.

Selected results from a few studies are sufficient to prove the significance of the influence of grazing. The work carried out by the Moorland Restoration Project team in the Peak District National Park clearly demonstrated the detrimental effects of grazing. Fenced heather-seeded areas (exclosures) were compared with equivalent unfenced heather-seeded areas. In practically every site, *Calluna* within the exclosure had performed better than the *Calluna* outside. Table 4.2 gives a comparison of heather performance in grazed and ungrazed areas at two sites.

Table 4.2 **The effect of grazing on the growth of heather in fenced and unfenced areas after spreading cut heather on to bare peat substrates. (compiled from Tallis & Yalden, 1983)**

Site (Peak District National Park, Derbyshire)	Age of plants (yrs)	Height of plants (mm)	Above-ground weight (g)
Burbage Moor:			
Fenced	2	78.9	0.37
Unfenced	2	45.6	0.10
Holme Moss S.W.:			
Fenced	3	91.2	0.31
Unfenced	3	34.4	0.06

Grazing also had an adverse effect on flowering of *Calluna*, survival of seedlings in the first year, and the survival of older established plants.   The flowering of *Deschampsia flexuosa* and the rate of spread of *Eriophorum angustifolium* were also adversely affected.

At Lee Moor in Devon, Gillham (1980) demonstrated that the effect of grazing by Dartmoor ponies and by sheep was relatively severe in the early stages of heathland restoration. Figure A1.1 in Appendix I shows the number of seedlings m^{-2} of *Calluna* and *Erica* spp. on grazed and ungrazed areas in the second year of the experiment. There is a striking difference in the population density of heathers, particularly in the treatments with sown companion grass species.

A field experiment carried out by Meaden (1983) at Moel Famau, Clwyd, provides further evidence of the impact of grazing by sheep. The area of upland heath (at an altitude of 350m) was extensively burnt in 1974, and recovery of the heathland vegetation was very poor. There was extensive surface erosion due to the poor vegetation cover (mainly bryophytes). The experiment was designed to test requirements for improvement of *Calluna* growth, namely exclusion of grazing, mineral nutrient input, *Calluna* seed input and sown companion grasses. Just two years after the start of the experiment, it was clear that grazing pressure alone was responsible for the poor regeneration of *Calluna* and other dwarf shrub species.

After two growing seasons, above-ground biomass of *Calluna* in the various treatments within the fenced area ranged from 2319 - 5494kg ha^{-1} whilst in the grazed experimental area the values were 200 - 1378kg ha^{-1}. Within the grazing exclosure, there was profuse flowering of heather in the second year. It is clear that at Moel Famau, even a moderate sheep stocking density was sufficient to virtually prevent establishment and growth of *Calluna* and other native heathland species on an almost bare substratum.

The question of how long protection from grazing is necessary after initial restoration has been carried out cannot be answered unequivo- cally. An experiment by the EAU at Robinson's Moss demonstrated that when the fences were removed after one year only, grazing damaged the young heather plants and the grass swards to such an extent that the restored areas of heather moorland did not survive and became increasingly eroded.

The restoration of the Scottish Gas pipeline across the Pentland Hills near Edinburgh involved maintaining boundary fences for many years after pipe installation. The fences were regularly checked, and were kept in a good stock-proof state. Six years after the initial restoration, one section of fence was removed. One year later (at the last observation), the condition of the heather moorland remained excellent.

It is difficult to forecast accurately the length of time that should be allowed, after initial restoration, before heathland vegetation can be safely grazed at sensible stocking rates. This will depend on the growth rate of *Calluna* and associated heathland species. At low altitudes and in southern locations, a grazing-free period of three or four years may be sufficient, but in more severely-exposed sites, protection from grazing for five or six years will be necessary. As a general rule, it would be sensible to protect all areas of restored heathland from large herbivores for a period of five years.

4.3.3 Conclusions

Newly restored areas of heathland are sensitive to grazing by large herbivores (sheep, horses and cattle). Damage is caused both by trampling and by grazing *per se*. Protection of restored heathland is essential, preferably for five years. Provision for maintenance of fences should be built-in to any restoration contract where grazing or trampling is seen as a potential problem.

ACKNOWLEDGEMENTS

This review was prepared for the Environmental Advisory Unit by Dr. P.D. Putwain (University of Liverpool), and edited by Dr. P.A.S. Rae (London Research Station, British Gas plc), both of whom would like to extend heartfelt thanks to all those who have contributed to its preparation, and in particular;

for case studies:

P. Anderson (Consultant Ecologist, Chinley, nr. Stockport)
M. Auld (Suffolk Naturalists Trust)
R.M. Bell (Environmental Advisory Unit, University of Liverpool)
R. Brown (North York Moors National Park)
M. Childs (Poole Borough Council)
N. Coppin (Wardle Armstrong, Newcastle-under-Lyme)
C. Down (University College, London)
J. Daniels (Countryside Commission)
P. Johnson (Ove Arup & Partners, London)
L.D. Owen (English China Clay International plc)
P. Packham (Public Services Agency, DoE)
H.W. Mackworth-Praed (National Trust)
M. Thomson (Ecologist, Clwyd County Council)

for photographs:

D.A.Gillham (Dept.of Botany, University of Liverpool) : Plates 1 & 12
D.M. Parker (Environmental Advisory Unit, University of Liverpool) :
            Plate 20

for figures and tables:

P.B. Park (London Research Station, British Gas plc)
The Nature Conservancy Council : Fig. 1.1
The Peak Park Joint Planning Board : Tables 2.1, 2.2, 3.5 & 3.6
J.E. Lowday (Consultant Ecologist, Dulverton, Somerset) : Table 2.3

for preparing the manuscript:

D. Peedell (London Research Station, British Gas plc).

Finally, considerable thanks are also extended to Dr. E.S. Pankhurst (London Research Station, British Gas plc) for her unstinting advice and guidance.

APPENDIX I

DETAILS OF CASE HISTORIES AND EXPERIMENTAL WORK

1.0 Quarries and mineral extraction sites

1.1 Lee Moor, near Plymouth, Devon (section 2.1.2)

In April 1976, experiments were set up to study the establishment of heathland species on china clay sand waste at Lee Moor, near Plymouth (National Grid Ref. SX 562613). The site is very close to the boundary of the Dartmoor National Park. The work was reported by Gillham (1980), and Putwain & Gillham (1988) whose major experiment was established in the following way.

Seed-rich topsoil (to a depth of 40-50 - 200mm) was stripped from well-grazed areas of heather moorland which were scheduled for imminent tipping of sand waste. Topsoil was removed using an excavator equipped with a '4 in 1' bucket. Large turves were broken up using a petrol-driven horticultural soil shredder, and the topsoil was spread to a depth of 25-30mm and was lightly compacted, on either raw sand waste or on 100mm of quarry overburden (subsoil) which had been previously spread on the sand waste (Plate 1).

Fertiliser (ICI No.5, 17:17:17) was applied at three rates equivalent to 0, 100, and 300 kg ha^{-1}, to 1 m^2 plots. Three different companion grass species were sown; *Agrostis castellana* cv. Highland (15 kg ha^{-1}), *Lolium perenne* cv. S24 (50 kg ha^{-1}), and *Festuca tenuifolia* (30 kg ha^{-1}).

Grazing ponies, cattle and sheep were excluded from half the experimental area, but an identical series of plots was left accessible to grazing animals.

Results were assessed after one, two, three, five and seven years. Figs. A1.1 and A1.2 show some of these results in terms of establishment of heather (*Calluna* plus *Erica* spp) after two years and seven years. *Agrostis curtisii* is very characteristic of heathlands in the south west, and seedling numbers of this species are shown

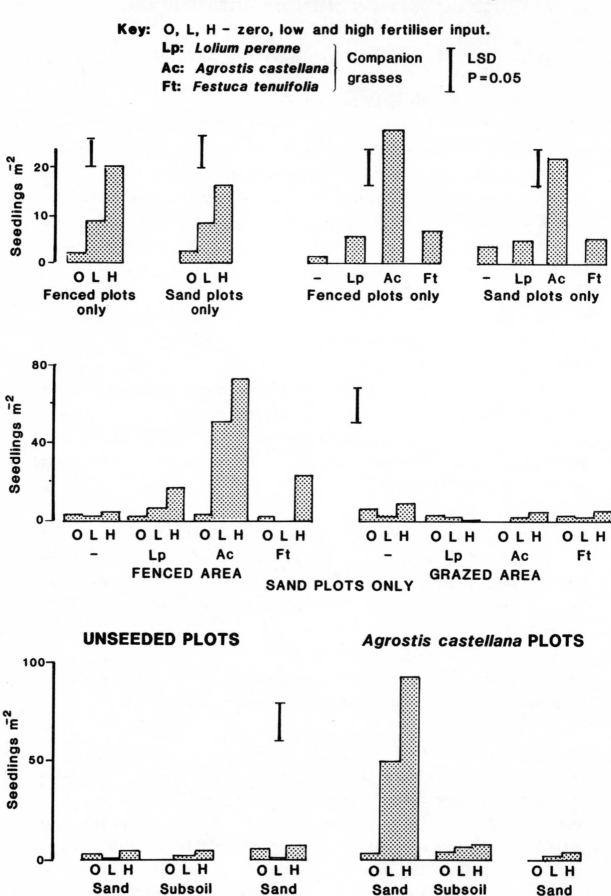

Fig. A1.1. Number of heather (*Calluna* plus *Erica* spp.) seedlings m̄² at Lee Moor, Devon. August 1978.

Key: O, L, H – zero, low and high fertiliser input.
Lp: *Lolium perenne*
Ac: *Agrostis castellana*   Companion grasses   LSD P=0.05
Ft: *Festuca tenuifolia*

Fig. A1.2. Heather restoration (Lee Moor, Devon). Percent cover of *Calluna* & *Erica* spp. after 7 years.

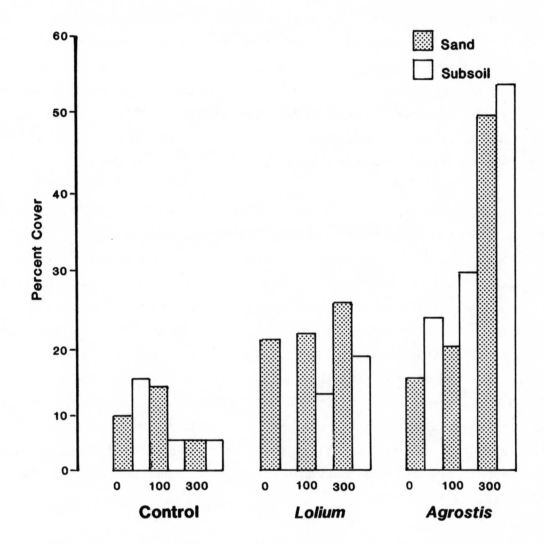

in Fig. Al.3. Percent cover of the important heathland plant species in 1983 (after seven years) is shown in Table Al.1.

After two years, the number of heather seedlings per m² was highest in the exclosure plots where *Agrostis castellana* was sown as a companion species. The grazed plots (all treatments) had a very low number of heather seedlings. Establishment of heather was initially better where the topsoil was spread directly onto the sand waste. The seedling establishment of other native species such as bristle-leaved bent-grass (*Agrostis curtisii*) and western gorse (*Ulex gallii*) was not influenced by the type of companion grass species, or by the substrate on which topsoil was spread.

However, after three years and again after five years, establishment and growth of *Calluna* and *Erica* spp tended to be successful in plots on the overburden substratum, particularly where *Agrostis* was the companion species. After seven years (1983), percent cover of heather was greatest on plots which had been sown with *Agrostis*, even though this species had almost disappeared. On treatments with no sown companion species, heather cover remained low and patchy. Where either *Lolium* or *Agrostis* had been sown originally, there was a response to fertiliser addition with respect to percent cover of *Calluna* and *Erica* spp. Percent cover of *Agrostis curtisii* was greater on subsoil plots, whilst other native heathland species were distributed more or less randomly across the experimental treatments, (Plate 2).

It was concluded that use of subsoil, companion grass (particularly *Agrostis castellana*) and a moderate to high fertiliser application ultimately gave the most well-balanced heathland community in terms of plant species composition (Plates 3 and 4). It is absolutely clear that at Lee Moor, protection from grazing for a period of five years was essential, because heathland reinstatement failed in the grazed plots.

Fig. A1.3. Number of seedlings m̄² of *Agrostis curtisii* within grazing exclosure at Lee Moor, Devon. August 1978.

Key as for Figure A.1.1

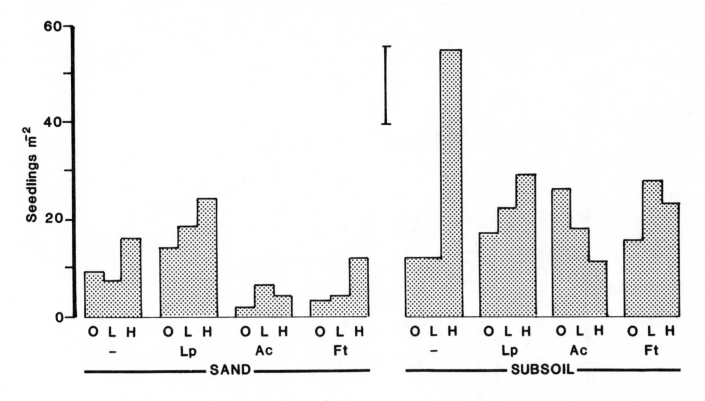

Table A 1.1   Percent cover of heathland species at Lee Moor in 1983, seven years after the establishment of the experiment.

Species	Experimental Treatment																	
	SUBSOIL									SAND								
	Fertiliser 0			Fertiliser 100			Fertiliser 300			Fertiliser 0			Fertiliser 100			Fertiliser 300		
	Con	S24	Ag	Con	S24	Ag	Con	S24	Ag	Con	S24	Ag	Con	S24	Ag	Con	S24	Ag
Calluna vulgaris	5.3	0.0	8.7	4.3	5.7	8.7	5.3	0.0	8.7	5.3	0.0	8.7	5.3	0.0	8.7	5.3	0.0	8.7
Erica spp	6.7	0.0	11.3	0.0	0.0	11.3	6.7	0.0	11.3	6.7	0.0	11.3	6.7	0.0	11.3	6.7	0.0	11.3
Ulex spp	39.7	59.3	41.3	71.0	59.3	41.3	39.7	59.3	41.3	39.7	59.3	41.3	39.7	59.3	41.3	39.7	59.3	41.3
Agrostis curtisii	16.7	36.0	27.7	20.0	36.0	27.7	16.7	36.0	27.7	16.7	36.0	27.7	16.7	36.0	27.7	16.7	36.0	27.7
Molinia caerulea	26.3	4.0	4.3	4.3	4.0	4.3	26.3	4.0	4.3	26.3	4.0	4.3	26.3	4.0	4.3	26.3	4.0	4.3
Potentilla erecta	0.0	0.7	1.0	0.3	0.7	1.0	0.0	0.7	1.0	0.0	0.7	1.0	0.0	0.7	1.0	0.0	0.7	1.0

Key

Con   –   Control; no added companion species

S24   –   Lolium perenne cv S24

Ag   –   Agrostis castellana

1.2   Blackhill Quarry, near Exmouth, Devon (section 2.1.2).

Larger scale heathland restoration was tried at Blackhill Quarry on an area of approximately 2ha, which had been regraded following extraction of sand and gravel.   In summer 1977, litter and topsoil were obtained from an adjacent area of heathland (c. 0.5ha) which was to be quarried in the near future. The area was first flail mown and then rotovated to a depth of 100mm.   The material was stripped and spread on the re-instatement area with an agricultural muck-spreader.   Two weeks later this area was hydroseeded with a mixture of grass and legume seeds and fertiliser.   The seed mixture was unnecessarily complex, comprising cultivars of *Agrostis*, *Festuca*, *Lolium* and *Poa* plus five different legume species, sown at a total rate of 140 kg ha^{-1}.

Fertiliser application was as follows:

Bonemeal	200 kg ha^{-1}
Enmag	100 kg ha^{-1}
Triple super phosphate	50 kg ha^{-1}
Nitro shell	100 kg ha^{-1}
Muriate of potash	50 kg ha^{-1}

Horticultural peat was also included as a mulch at a rate of 800 kg ha^{-1}.

After two years, an open mixed species sward had established, including young *Calluna* plants with an average ground cover of 15%.   Overall ground cover was *circa* 50%, and other species present in the vegetation were bell heather (*Erica cinerea*), wavy hair-grass (*Deschampsia flexuosa*), western gorse (*Ulex gallii*), purple moor grass (*Molinia caerulea*) and heath bedstraw (*Galium saxatile*).

The initial appearance of the restored area was not ideal, since vegetation tended to establish in strips corresponding to the path of the muck-spreader. Also, sown species were becoming moribund and it was apparent that the complex seed mixture that had been used was not necessary. However, it seemed at the time that a visually satisfactory restoration of heathland vegetation, compatible with adjacent lowland heathland, might be achieved in a further two or three years. Grazing animals did not have access to the site, and this was clearly beneficial to plant establishment. The area has since been left unmanaged, and is now unsatisfactory as heathland restoration. There has been considerable establishment and growth of gorse (*Ulex europaeus*), so that about 30% of the whole area is covered. Also some patches have 20-30% bare ground. Use of the chemical triclopyr (Garlon 4) to kill the gorse selectively would improve the restoration as a whole. An application of Enmag fertiliser (rate 200-300 kg ha^{-1}) would also improve the growth of native species (other than *Ulex*), and increase vegetation cover where bare areas occur.

2.0   Construction : reservoirs and containment dams

2.1 Robinson's Moss, Derbyshire (section 2.2.2)

Robinson's Moss is an area of deep blanket peat, dissected by deep channels, at an altitude of 480m (Plate 6). The EAU carried out some expermental work here for containment dams, bunds and construction work related to a proposed CEGB power station at Longdendale. The first series of experiments was set up in May 1980, on sites which included bare peat substrates on level and sloping ground, a constructed peat lagoon, and a mineral area. The same basic experimental design was used for each site.

The following treatments were applied in factorial combinations:

1.   Introduction of propagules of moorland and blanket mire species;
      there were three treatments:
      (a) Macerated vegetation : blanket mire vegetation stripped from
           a nearby area, coarsely chopped and respread to an average
           depth of 25-30 mm.
      (b) Sowing harvested capsules of *Calluna* (45 kg ha^{-1}) and
           seed of *Deschampsia flexuosa* (30 kg ha^{-1}).
      (c) Control - undisturbed bare peat.

2.   Sowing commercial grass cultivars as companion species; the two
      alternative treatments were plus or minus companion species.

      The species mixture (% by weight) was *Agrostis castellana*
      (85%), *Festuca rubra* cv. S59 (7.5%), and *Lolium perenne*
      cv.S23 (7.5%), sown at a rate of 20 kg ha^{-1}.

The plus or minus companion grasses treatment was combined with plus or minus fertiliser and ground limestone. The fertiliser treatment consisted of finely ground ICI No.5 (17:17:17) at a rate of 200 kg ha^{-1}, combined with superphosphate at a rate of 100 kg ha^{-1}. Ground limestone was applied at a rate of 2,500 kg ha^{-1}. This and the fertiliser were evenly spread over the experimental plots (1.5m x 1.5m) at the same time as the grass seed was sown.

These experiments were monitored in spring and autumn for six growing seasons from May 1980 until October 1985.

Three further large scale experiments were established in April 1983, on different substrates, namely a mineral area, sloping bare peat and level bare peat. The peat substrates were divided into three sections to allow roll-back of fencing and exposure to grazing by sheep after various time intervals. The mineral substrate was divided into five sections. Within each section, randomly selected small plots were either covered with macerated surface vegetation or were planted with heather plants grown in paper tubes. The heather plants had been raised from cuttings at Liverpool University Botanic Gardens, and grown in trays each containing 200 plants; the approximate cost of production was 10p for each plant.

The rest of the areas were sown with the following seed mixture:

Deschampsia flexuosa	40 kg ha^{-1}
Agrostis castellana cv. Highland	20 kg ha^{-1}
Secale cereale (Rye)	50 kg ha^{-1}

Fertiliser was applied over the whole experimental area at the following rates per hectare:

ICI No.5 (17:17:17)	200 kg
Super phosphate	100 kg
Ground limestone	2500 kg

After six growing seasons, the results of the first set of experiments broadly indicated that it would be possible to restore heather moorland and mire vegetation using the existing vegetation and the top layer of peat (150mm) macerated and re-spread, although addition of heather litter and cut vegetation bearing seed capsules might also give successful results. Certain companion grass species (e.g. *Deschampsia flexuosa* and *Agrostis castellana*) would not only stabilise the peat surface, but would also allow native moorland species to become established from vegetative fragments (e.g. *Vaccinium myrtillus*, *Empetrum nigrum*), or from seed (e.g. *Calluna*). Some initial input of lime and fertiliser (see Tables A1.2 and A1.3 for details) was necessary to maintain the plant species assemblage for two growing seasons. Regeneration of *Calluna* was more effective from litter or macerated vegetation plus top peat, than from sowing of commercially purchased seed capsules. (Plates 7 and 8).

The small plot experiments showed that mobile peat surfaces can be stabilised effectively using a grass seed mixture plus adequate input of ground limestone and fertiliser. A stable plant community consisting of native moorland species will regenerate within the sown grass matrix (if fertiliser input is only moderate), and this apparently becomes self-perpetuating with just an initial input of fertiliser plus a follow-up treatment after three years.

The larger scale experiments showed (after three years) that the procedures can be scaled-up and remain effective. In addition the impact of grazing was substantially detrimental (first exposure after 18 months) to the early development of the moorland vegetation. *Calluna* was particularly hard hit. (Plates 9 and 10).

The growth and development of *Calluna* planted in paper tubes was excellent (when protected from sheep), and survival was also very good. The heather plants flowered and set seed during the second growing season (Plate 11). When heathers are planted in patches within a grass matrix, they act as a local source for further colonisation and spread. The grass matrix of *Deschampsia flexuosa* also established satisfactorily, and by summer 1985, seedlings of *Calluna* had begun to appear around the periphery of the patches of tubed heather plants.

Table A1.2   **Experimental treatments established on deep peat at**
Robinson's Moss, May 1980

Companion grasses	Source of native plant propagules	Addition of mineral nutrients and limestone
+	comemrcial seed	+
+	commercial seed	−
+	macerated vegetation	+
+	macerated vegetation	−
+	none	+
+	none	−
−	commercial seed	+
−	commercial seed	−
−	macerated vegetation	+
−	macerated vegetation	−
−	none	+
−	none	−

Companion grass species mixture by weight:

Agrostis castellana cv. Highland	85%
Festuca rubra cv. S59	7.5%
Lolium perenne cv. S23	7.5%

Macerated vegetation applied at an average depth of 25-30 mm.

Sowing rate of commercial seed of native species:

Deschampsia flexuosa	30 kg ha^{-1}
Calluna vulgaris	45 kg ha^{-1}

Application rate of mineral nutrients:

ICI No.5 (17% N, 17% P_2O_5, 17% K_2O)	200 kg ha^{-1}
Super phosphate	100 kg ha^{-1}

Application rate of ground limestone: 1,500 kg ha^{-1}

Table A1.3   **Further experimental treatments established at**
Robinson's Moss, May 1980

Companion grasses	Macerated vegetation	Addition of mineral nutrients and limestone
+	+	+
+	+	−
+	−	+
+	−	−

Companion grass species mixture by weight:

Festuca rubra cv S59	25%
Lolium perenne cv S23	25%
L. perenne x *L. mutiflorum* hybrid	25%
Lolium hybrid cv Augusta	25%

Sowing rate: 20 kg ha^{-1}

Macerated vegetation applied at an average depth of 25-30 mm.
Application rate of mineral nutrients:

ICI No.5 (17% N, 17% P_2O_5, 17% K_2O)	300 kg ha^{-1}
Super phosphate	150 kg ha^{-1}

Application rate of ground limestone: 4,000 kg ha^{-1}

Additional fertiliser treatment, May 1981

All plots which received an initial fertiliser treatment in May 1980
were divided into two equal sub-plots. One randomly selected sub-
plot had fertiliser applied at half the rate which was originally
applied in May 1980.

(i)   ICI No.5 (17:17:17) 100 kg ha^{-1} plus Super phosphate 50 kg ha^{-1}
or

(ii) ICI No.5 150 kg ha^{-1} plus Super phosphate 75 kg ha^{-1}.

The results at Robinson's Moss demonstrated the relative effectiveness of several different ways of introducing heather into the plant community:

a) use of macerated surface vegetation plus the top few centimetres of peat - very effective

b) use of broadcast heather litter - effective

c) use of broadcast seed of *Calluna* (in harvested capsules) - less effective, and colonisation relatively slow

d) use of heather plants raised in paper tubes (from cuttings or litter) - very effective but can only be employed in patches, or at a low planting density.

APPENDIX II

RECOMMENDED SEED MIXTURES SUITABLE AS COMPANION SPECIES FOR *CALLUNA* AND OTHER NATIVE HEATHLAND PLANTS, AND IN SOME SITES APPROPRIATE FOR EROSION CONTROL. (PERCENT BY WEIGHT IN MIXTURE).

SPECIES (for cultivars see Table 3.4)	DEEP ACID PEAT		SHALLOW ACID PEAT, HEATHER MOOR/GRASS HEATH	DRY LOWLAND HEATH		WET/HUMID LOWLAND HEATH
	Stable areas	Eroding areas		Stable areas	Eroding areas	
Deschampsia flexuosa	40	25	30	10		10
Festuca ovina/ F. tenuifolia			20	20	15	20
Festuca longifolia				10	15	
F. rubra ssp commutata ‡				20	30	
F. rubra ssp litoralis	30	30	10			
Agrostis castellana	40	35	30	30	40	40
A. vinealis =*A.canina ssp montana*‡			10	10		
A. canina =*A.canina ssp canina* ‡						30
Overall rate of application (kg ha⁻¹)	15	25	15-20	10-15	15-25	

‡ nomenclature according to Hubbard, 1968

APPENDIX II (cont'd.)

SUPPLIERS OF COMPANION GRASS SPECIES AT COMMERCIAL PRICES

SPECIES (for cultivars see Table 3.4)	SUPPLIER	AVAILABILITY (1987)	APPROXIMATE PRICE(per kg) (1987)
Deschampsia flexuosa	W W Johnson	Difficult to obtain	£8.00 to £17.00
F. ovina	W W Johnson Emorsgate	Supplies O.K.	£1.50 to £4.70
Festuca tenuifolia	W W Johnson, Mommersteeg	Some difficulty	£1.50 to £5.00
F. longifolia	Picard, BSH, Mommersteeg	Slight shortage	£2.00 to £4.00
F. rubra ssp *commutata* ‡	Picard, Mommersteeg, W W Johnson, BSH, Pope & Chapman	Supplies O.K.	£1.40 to £3.00
F. rubra ssp *litoralis*	BSH, Mommersteeg Pope & Chapman	Supplies O.K.	£2.20 to £3.00
F.rubra ssp *pruinosa*	W W Johnson, Emorsgate	Supplies O.K.	£3.00 to £3.50
Agrostis castellana	BSH, Picard, Mommersteeg	Supplies O.K.	£1.60 to £3.00
A. vinealis (= *A.canina* ssp *montana*)‡	Mommersteeg	Extremely hard to obtain	---
A. canina (= *A.canina* ssp *canina*) ‡	Mommersteeg	Difficult to obtain	---
A. capillaris (= *A.tenuis*)‡	W W Johnson, Mommersteeg	Supply shortage	£3.00 to £7.00
Lolium perenne	Numerous	Easy to obtain	£0.84 to £4.45

‡ nomenclature according to Hubbard, 1968.

APPENDIX II (cont'd.)

ADDRESSES OF SEED SUPPLIERS

British Seed Houses Ltd.,
Bewsey Industrial Estate,
Pitt Street,
Warrington,
Cheshire WA5 5LE   Tel: (0925) 54411

W.W. Johnson & Son Ltd.,
Boston,
Lincs PE1 8AD   Tel (0205) 65051

Emorsgate Seeds,
Emorsgate,
Terrington St. Clement,
Kings Lynn,
Norfolk PE34 4NY   Tel: (0553) 829028

Mommersteeg International Ltd.,
Station Road,
Finedon,
Wellingborough,
Northants NN9 5NT   Tel: (0933) 680674

J. Picard & Co Ltd.,
11, Mill Street,
London SE1   Tel: (01) 237 5377

Pope & Chapman Ltd.,
13/19 Hockerill Street,
Bishop's Stortford,
Herts   Tel: (0279) 53261

Plate 19. An area of successfully regenerated heathland in Surrey
which has developed on a graded area similar to that
shown in Plate 18. This area is managed by occasional
cutting.

Plate 20. Using a forage harvester to cut heather and collect
seed capsules.

APPENDIX III

HERBICIDE SUPPLIERS

Atlas Interlates Ltd..
Fraser Road,
Erith,
Kent DA8 1PN   Tel: (03224) 32255

Battle, Hayward & Bower Ltd,.
Victoria Chemical Works,
Crofton Drive,
Allenby Road Industrial Estate,
Lincoln LN3 4NP   Tel: (0522) 29206/7

Chipman Ltd.,
The Goods Yard,
Horsham,
Sussex RH12 2NR   Tel: (0403) 69341-5

Dupont UK Ltd.,
Agricultural Chemicals Dept.,
Wedgewood Way,
Stevenage,
Herts. SG1 4ON   Tel: (0438) 822561

May & Baker Ltd.,
Agrochemicals Division,
Regent House,
Hubert Road,
Brentwood,
Essex   Tel: (0277) 261414

Monsanto plc.,
Agricultural Division,
Thames Tower,
Burley Way,
Leicester LE1 3TP   Tel: (0533) 20864

Pan Britannica Industries Ltd.,
Britannica House,
Waltham Cross,
Herts. EN8 7DY   Tel: (0992) 23691

APPENDIX IV

GROUPS AND ORGANISATIONS CONCERNED
WITH HEATHLAND RESTORATION

Cannock Chase Country Park,
Staffordshire County Council,
Martin Street,
Stafford

Countryside Commission,
John Dower House,
Crescent Place
Cheltenham
Glos. GL50 3RA

English China Clay International plc
John Keay House,
St. Austell,
Cornwall PI28 4DJ

Institute of Terrestrial Ecology,
(Natural Environment Research Council),
Administrative Headquarters,
Monks Wood Experimental Station,
Abbots Ripton,
Huntingdon PE17 2LS

National Trust,
36, Queen Anne's Gate,
London SW1H 9AS

Nature Conservancy Council,
(Nature Conservation),
Northminster House,
Peterborough,
Cambs. PE1 1UA

North York Moors National Park,
The Old Vicarage,
Bondagte,
Helmsley,
York

APPENDIX IV (cont'd)

Peak Park Joint Planning Board,
Peak District National Park,
Alden House,
Bakewell,
Derbyshire

Public Services Agency, (PSA)
Department of the Environment,
2, Marsham Street,
London SW1P 3EB

Royal Society for Nature Conservation,
The Green,
Nettleham,
Lincs. LN2 2NR

> Dorset Naturalists Trust,
> 39, Christchurch Road,
> Bournemouth,
> Dorset BH1 3NS
>
> Suffolk Trust for Nature Conservation,
> The Sandlings Project,
> Park Cottage,
> Saxmundham,
> Suffolk IP17 1DQ
>
> Surrey Trust for Nature Conservation,
> The Administration Office STNC,
> Hatchlands,
> East Clandon,
> Guildford,
> Surrey GU4 7RT

Yorkshire Dales National Park,
(The Three Peaks Project),
Colvend,
Henden Road,
Grassington BD23 5LB

154

REFERENCES

Anon. (1973). <u>Report of the Ball Clay Working Party, Russell Quay, Arne</u>. Mineral Project Pilot Study. Dorset County Planning Dept./EEC Ball Clays Ltd. December 1973.

Anon. (1977). <u>Heath fires in Dorset 1976.</u> A report and recommendations by the Dorset Naturalists' Trust and the Royal Society for the Protection of Birds. January 1977.

Bannister, A. (1987). Control of pesticides regulations. <u>Landscape Design</u> No.169, 53

Bannister, P. (1964a). The water relations of certain heath plants with reference to their ecological amplitude. I. Introduction: germination and establishment. <u>J. Ecol.</u>, <u>52</u>, 423-432.

Bannister, P. (1964b). The water relations of certain heath plants with reference to their ecological amplitude. II. Field studies. <u>J. Ecol.</u>, <u>52</u>, 481-497.

Bannister, P. (1965). Biological flora of the British Isles. *Erica cinerea* (L) <u>J. Ecol.</u>,<u>53</u>, 527-542.

Bannister, P. (1966). Biological flora of the British Isles. *Erica tetralix* (L) <u>J. Ecol.</u>,<u>54</u>, 795-813.

Bayfield, N.G. & Brookes, B.S. (1979). Effects of repeated use of an area of heather (*Calluna vulgaris* (L) Hull) moor at Kindrogan, Scotland, for teaching purposes. <u>Biol. Conserv.</u>, <u>16</u>, 31-41.

Bayfield, N.G. & McGowan,G.M. (1986). <u>Three Peaks Project. ITE Report No.1. Footpath Survey 1986</u>. Yorkshire Dales National Park, Grassington, Yorks.

Bayfield, N.G. & Miller, G.R. (1986). <u>Three Peaks Project. ITE Report No.2. Reinstatement Trials 1986</u>. Yorkshire Dales National Park, Grassington, Yorks.

Birse, E.L., (1968). <u>Hill-land vegetation in Scotland</u>. Proc.Symp. Hill-land Productivity - European Grassland Federation. 4 pp July 1968.

Brooks, D.R. & Bell, L.C. (1984). The technology of rehabilitation following mineral sands mining on North Stradbroke Island. In <u>Focus on Stradbroke</u> (eds. R.J. Coleman, J. Covacevich & P. Davie) pp 184-194. Boolarong Publications, Brisbane.

Brooks, D.R. & Yates, D.J. (1980). Ecosystem development in frontal dunes after mining. <u>Landline</u>, <u>4</u>, 2-3. Australian Mining Industry Council, Canberra.

Burden, R.F. (1979). Landscape scientist in a county planning office. <u>Landscape Design,</u> <u>126,</u> 9.

Chapman, S.B. (1967). Nutrient budgets for a dry heath ecosystem in the south of England. <u>J.Ecol.</u>, <u>55</u>, 677-689

REFERENCES

Chapman, S.B. (1970). The nutrient content of the soil and root system of a dry heath ecosystem. J.Ecol., 58, 445-452.

Champress, S.S. & Morris, K. (1948). The population of buried viable seeds in relation to contrasting pasture and soil types. J. Ecol., 36, 149-173.

Chippindale, H.G. & Milton, W.E.J. (1934). On the viable seeds present in soil beneath pastures. J. Ecol., 22, 508-531.

Clapham, A.R. Tutin, T.G.; & Moore D.M. (1987). Flora of the British Isles. Cambridge University Press. 3rd edn.

Clark, S.S. (1975). The effect of sand mining on coastal heath vegetation in New South Wales. Proceedings Ecological Society of Australia, 9, 1-16.

Commonwealth Agricultural Bureaux, & British Crop Protection Council, (1988). The U.K. Pesticide Guide. CAB International, Wallingford & BCPC, Bracknell.

Countryside Commission (1978). Upland Land Use in England and Wales Countryside Commission, CCP 111.

Countryside Commission (1985a). Cannock Chase 1979-1984 A country park plan on trial, CCP 181 56pp

Countryside Commission (1985b). Technical Report 2. Heathland Management trials at Brindley Heath. CCP 183.

Cruickshank, J.G. (1972). Soil Geography. David and Charles. Newton Abbot.

Daniels, J.L. (1983). Bracken control in mixed heather and bracken stands. In Heathland Management in Amenity Areas, CCP 159 24-25

Davis, B.N.K. (1976). Wildlife, urbanisation and industry. Biol. Conserv., 10, 249-292.

Department of the Environment & University of Liverpool, Environmental Advisory Unit (1986). Transforming our Waste land : The way forward. H.M.S.O.

Dimbleby, G.W. (1962). The development of British heathlands and their soils. Oxf. For.Mem., 23, 1-21. Clarendon Press.

Du Croz, W. & Schofield M. (1983). The construction of a pipeline by Esso Petroleum Co.Ltd. In: Focus on Nature Conservation No. 2 Heathland Management. (Ed. L. Farrell), Nature Conservancy Council, pp. 111-127.

Etherington, J.R. (1981). Limestone heaths in south-west Britain : their soils and the maintenance of their calcicole-calcifuge mixtures. J.Ecol. 69, 277-294

Farrell, L. (1983). The current state and objectives of management of British heaths. In : Heathland Management in Amenity Areas. CCP 159.

Fitzpatrick, E.A. (1967). Soil nomenclature and classification. Geoderma 1, 91-105.

Fyfe-Maxwell, D. & Patrick, P.S. (1966). The English Heather Garden. MacDonald, London.

Gilbert, O.L. & Wathern, P. (1976). Towards production of extensive Calluna swards. Landscape Design, 114, 35.

Gillham, D.A. & Putwain, P.D. (1977). Restoring moorland disturbed by pipeline installation. Landscape Design, 119, 34-36.

Gillham, D.A. 1980. The conservation and restoration of heathland vegetation disturbed by industrial operations. Ph.D. Thesis. University of Liverpool.

Gimingham, C.H. (1972). Ecology of Heathlands. Chapman and Hall. London.

Gore, A.J.P. (1975). An experimental modification of upland peat vegetation. Journal of Applied Ecology, 12, 349-366

Gore, A.J.P. & Godfrey M, (1981). Reclamation of eroded peat in the Pennines. J. Ecol. 69, 85-96

Green, B.H. (1974). Heathland conservation and management. In: Southern Heathlands Symposium, pp. 60-64. Surrey Naturalists' Trust, 1976.

Grubb, P.J; Green, H.E. & Merrifield, R.C.J. (1969). The ecology of chalk heath: its relevance to the calcicole-calcifuge and soil acidification problems. J. Ecol., 57., 175-212.

Hansen, K. (1964). Studies on the regeneration of heath vegetation after burning off. Bot. Tidsskr., 60, 1-41.

Harper, J.L. (1971). Grazing, fertilisers and pesticides in the management of grasslands. In : The Scientific Management of Animal and Plant Communities for Conservation, eds. E.Duffey & A.S. Watt, pp 15-32, Blackwell Scientific Publications, Oxford.

Harper, J.L. (1977). Population Biology of Plants. Academic Press.

Heil, G.W. & Diemont, W.H. (1983). Raised nutrient levels change heathland into grassland. Vegetatio, 53, 113-120.

Helsper, H.P.G., Glenn-Lewin, D. & Werger, M.J.A. (1983). Early regeneration of Calluna heathland under various fertilisation treatments. Oecologia (Berlin), 58, 208-214

H.M.S.O. (1976). Aggregates: the way ahead. Report of the Verney Committee.

Hobbs. R.J., & Gimingham. C.H. (1987). Vegetation fire and herbivore interactions in heathland. Advances in Ecological Research. 16, 87-173.

Holliday, R.J.; Gillham, D.A.;Putwain, P.D. & Hogg, W. (1979). The restoration of heather moorland following severe disturbance - a case study of the installation of a gas pipeline in the Pentland Hills, near Edinburgh, Landscape Design, 126, 33-36.

Hubbard, C.E. (1968). <u>Grasses</u> 2nd edition. Penguin Books Ltd.,

King, J. (1960). Observations on the seedling establishment and growth
    of *Nardus stricta* in burned Callunetum. <u>J</u>. <u>Ecol</u>., <u>48</u> 667-677.

Laar, H. van de (1978). <u>The Heather Garden.</u> Collins, London

Lowday, J.E. (1983). Bracken control on lowland heaths.
    <u>Focus on Nature Conservation No. 2. Heathland Management</u>
    (Ed. L. Farrell). Nature Conservancy Council. 68-73.

Lowday, J.E. (1984). The restoration of heathland vegetation after
    control of dense bracken by asulam. <u>Aspects of Applied Biology, 5,</u>
    <u>Weed Control and Vegetation Management in Forests and Amenity</u>
    <u>Areas,</u> 283-290.

Lowday, J.E. (1984a). The effects of cutting and asulam on the frond and
    rhizome characteristics of bracken (*Pteridium aquilinum* (L)
    Kuhn). <u>Aspects of Applied Biology</u>, <u>5</u>, 275-281.

Lowday, J.E. (1984b). The restoration of heathland vegetation after
    control of dense bracken by asulam. <u>Aspects of Applied Biology</u>, <u>5</u>,
    283-290.

Marrs, R.H. (1983a). Scrub control on lowland heaths. <u>Focus on Nature</u>
    <u>Conservation No. 2 Heathland Management</u> (Ed. L. Farrell) Nature
    Conservancy Council. 59-67.

Marrs, R.H. (1983b). The control of birch and pine. <u>Heathland</u>
    <u>Management in Amenity Areas</u>. Ed.J.L. Daniels Countryside
    Commission CCP 159.

Marrs, R.H. (1984a). The use of herbicides for nature conservation.
    <u>Aspects of Applied Biology</u>. <u>5</u>, 265-274.

Marrs, R.H. (1984b). Birch control on lowland heaths: Mechanical control
    and the application of selective herbicides by foliar spray.
    <u>Journal of Applied Ecology</u>, <u>21</u>, 703-716.

Marrs, R.H. (1985a). Birch control by the treatment of cut stumps with
    herbicides. <u>Aboricultural Journal</u>, <u>9</u>, 173-182.

Marrs, R.H. (1985b). The effects of potential bracken and scrub
    herbicides on lowland *Calluna* and grass heath communities in
    East Anglia, U.K. <u>Biological Conservation</u>, <u>32</u>, 13-32.

Marrs, R.H. (1987). Studies on the conservation of lowland *Calluna*
    heaths I. Control of birch and bracken and its effect on heath
    vegetation. <u>Journal of Applied Ecology</u>, <u>24</u>, 163-175

Marrs, R.H. (1987). Studies on the conservation of lowland *Calluna*
    heaths II. Regeneration of *Calluna*, and its relation to
    bracken infestation. <u>Journal of Applied Ecology</u>, <u>24</u>, 177-189

Marrs, R.H. & Lowday, J.E. (1981). <u>Interim report from the Institute of</u>
    <u>Terrestrial Ecology to the Nature Conservancy Council.</u>
    NCC/NERC contract HP3/03/142.

Meaden, D.P. (1983). The Restoration and Creation of Heather Moorland
    Vegetation. Ph.D thesis, University of Liverpool.

Miles, J. (1973). Natural recolonisation of experimentally bared soil in
    Callunetum in North East Scotland. J. Ecol., 61, 399-412.

Miles, J. (1974). Effects of experimental interference with stand
    structure on establishment of seedlings in Callunetum.
    J. Ecol. 62, 675-688.

Miller, G.R. (1968). Evidence for selective feeding on fertilised plots
    by red grouse, hares and rabbits. Journal of Wildlife Management,
    32, 849-853.

Miller, G.R. (1979). Quantity and quality of the annual production of
    shoots and flowers by Calluna vulgaris in north east Scotland.
    Journal of Ecology, 67, 109-129.

Miller, G.R., Watson, A. and Jenkins, D. (1970). Response of red grouse
    Populations to experimental improvement of their food. Animal
    Populations in Relation to their Food Resources. (Ed. A. Watson).
    pp 232-235. Blackwell, Oxford. University of Aberdeen.

Ministry of Agriculture, Fisheries and Food, & Health and Safety
    Executive. (1988). Pesticides 1988. due Feb. '88.

Moffat, J.D. (1973). A study of the ecology of pipelines. M.Sc. thesis,
    University of Aberdeen.

Moffat, J.D. (1975a). Pipeline installation: problems, effects and
    improvements. Landscape Design, 112, 29-31.

Moffat, J.D. (1975b). Pipeline installation and its effects.
    Landowning in Scotland, Journal of the Scottish Landowners
    Federation, 158, 13-20.

Moore, N.W. (1962). The heaths of Dorset and their conservation.
    J.Ecol., 50, 369-391.

Munro, J.M.M., Davies, D.A. & Morgan, T.E. (1972). Research on pasture
    improvement potential at Pant-y-dwr Hill Centre. Report, Welsh
    Plant Breeding Station, 1972, 209-228.

National Trust (1986). Kinder : The first four years. The National
    Trust, High Peak Estate.

National Turfgrass Council & National Association of Agricultural
    Contractors. (1987). Pesticides. Codes of Practice for the Use of
    Approved Pesticides in Amenity Areas.

Nature Conservancy Council (1977). Nature Conservation and Agriculture.
    Nature Conservancy Council, London.

Nature Conservancy Council (1984). Nature Conservation in Great Britain.
    N.C.C., Peterborough

North York Moors National Park Committee (1980). Moorland Research
    1977-1979. North York Moors National Park. 44pp.

North York Moors National Park (1986). Moorland Management. N.Y.M.N.P.
    Helmsley, York.

O'Connor, B., Flint, D.E., & Aquilina, M. (1987). The control of bracken
    with sulphonyl-urea herbicides. Proceedings 1987, British Crop
    Protection Conference - Weeds. 757-764.

Phillips, J., Yalden, D., & Tallis, J.H. (eds.) (1981) Peak District
        Moorland Erosion Study, Phase I Report. 274 pp, Peak Park Joint
        Planning Board, Bakewell, Derbyshire.

Porchester, Lord (1977). A study of Exmoor, HMSO, London.

Putwain, P.D., Gilham, D.A. & Holliday, R.J. (1982). Restoration of
        heather moorland and lowland heathland, with special reference to
        pipelines, Env. Cons., 9, 225-235.

Putwain, P.D. & Gillham D.A. (1988). Restoration of heather moorland
        landscape on china clay wastes in South Devon. Landscape Design
        (in press).

Pyatt, D.G. (1970) Soil Groups of Upland Forests. Forestry Commission:
        Forest Record No.71. HMSO.

Ratcliffe, D.A. (1974) Ecological effects of mineral exploitation in the
        United Kingdom and their significance to nature conservation.
        Proc. R.Soc. Lond. A., 339, 355-72.

Ratcliffe, D.A. (1977). A Nature Conservation Review, ed.
        D.A.Ratcliffe, vols. 1 & 2. Cambridge University Press.

Rawes, M. & Williams, R. (1973). Production and utilisation of
        Calluna and Eriophorum. Potassium Institute Ltd.
        Colloquium Proceedings No. 3, 115-120.

Roberts, R.D. & Bradshaw, A.D. (1979). Hydraulic seeding. Techniques
        No.49. Landscape Design, 156, 42-47.

Rose, F. (1974). The vegetation of heaths. In: Southern Heathlands
        Symposium. pp. 13-22. Surrey Naturalists' Trust. 1976.

Singleton, G. (1975). Industry and the National Parks. A case study of
        Snowdonia. Landscape Design, 112, 18-21.

Streeter, D.T. (1975). Frensham Common Country Park. Landscape
        Restoration. Interim Report. Nov. 1975. University of Sussex.

SVEAG (The Sullom Voe Environmental Advisory Group) (1976). Oil terminal
        at Sullom Voe. Environmental Impact Assessment. SVEAG, May 1976,
        Thuleprint Ltd., Sandwick, Shetland.

Tallis, J.H. (1982). The Moorland Erosion Project in the Peak Park. In
        Moorlands: Wildlife Conservation Amenity and Recreation.
        Recreation Ecology Res. Group. Report No. 8, 27-36.

Tallis, J.H. & Yalden, D.W. (1983). Peak District Moorland Restoration
        Project, Phase 2 Report: Revegetation Trials. Peak Park Joint
        Planning Board, Bakewell, Derbyshire, 95pp.

Tansley, A.G. (1939). The British Islands and their Vegetation. Cambridge.

Thomas, A.S. (1957). Nature of chalk heath soils. Nature, Lond., 179, 545-546.

Tuck, M.V. (1979). The oil pipeline on Hartland Moor National Nature Reserve. Nature Conservancy Council Internal Report.

Wagg, C.J. (1974). Heathland conservation for leisure use. In: Southern Heathlands Symposium, pp.57-59. Surrey Naturalists' Trust, 1976.

Wallace, R (1917). Heather and Moor Burning for Grouse and Sheep. Edinburgh.

Wathern, P. (1976). The Ecology of Development Sites. Ph.D. Thesis, University of Sheffield.

Watson, A. & O'Hare, P.J. (1979). Red Grouse populations on experimentally treated and untreated Irish Bog. Journal of Applied Ecology, 16, 433-452.

Webb, N.R. & Haskins, L.E. (1980). An ecological survey of heathlands in the Poole Basin, Dorset, England in 1978. Biol. Consv. 17, 281-296.

Webb, N.R. (1986). Heathlands. the New Naturalist. Collins, London 223 pp.

Whittaker, E. & Gimingham, C.H. (1962). The effects of fire on regeneration of Calluna vulgaris (L) Hull from seed. J.Ecol., 50, 815-822.

Williams, G.H., & Davis D.H.K. (1987). A Sulphonyl-urea mixture for Pteridium control. Proceedings 1987 British Crop Protection Conference - Weeds. 765-772.

Yates, E.M. (1974). The distribution of heaths. In: Southern Heathlands Symposium: pp.7-12. Surrey Naturalists' Trust, 1976.

Zehetmayr, J.W.L. (1960). Afforestation of upland heaths. Forestry Commission Bulletin No. 32. Edinburgh: HMSO.